BTEC FIRST

REVISE BTEC

Sport

Unit 1 Fitness for Sport and Exercise

Unit 7 Anatomy and Physiology for Sports Performance

REVISION WORKBOOK

Series Consultant: Harry Smith   Authors: Adam Gledhill and Sally Hillier

THE REVISE BTEC SERIES

| BTEC First in Sport Revision Guide | 9781446906705 |
| BTEC First in Sport Revision Workbook | 9781446906712 |

This Workbook is designed to complement your classroom
and home learning, and to help prepare you for the test.
It does not include all the content and skills needed for the
complete course. It is designed to work in combination
with Pearson's main BTEC First series.

Gower College Swansea
Library
Coleg Gŵyr Abertawe
Llyrfgell

To find out more visit:
www.pearsonschools.co.uk/revise

ALWAYS LEARNING   **PEARSON**

Published by Pearson Education Limited, Edinburgh Gate, Harlow, Essex, CM20 2JE.

www.pearsonschoolsandfecolleges.co.uk

Copies of official specifications for all Pearson qualifications may be found on the website: www.edexcel.com

Text © Pearson Education Limited 2014
Typeset by Tech-Set Ltd, Gateshead
Original illustrations © Pearson Education Limited
Cover photo/illustration by Miriam Sturdee

The rights of Adam Gledhill and Sally Hillier to be identified as authors of this work has been asserted by them in accordance with the Copyright, Designs and Patents Act 1988.

First published 2014

17 16 15 14
10 9 8 7 6 5 4 3 2 1

British Library Cataloguing in Publication Data
A catalogue record for this book is available from the British Library

ISBN 978 1 4469 0671 2

Printed in Slovakia by Neografia

Acknowledgements

The publisher would like to thank the following for their kind permission to reproduce their photographs:
(Key: b-bottom; c-centre; l-left; r-right; t-top)

Alamy Images: Dan Galic 52tc, 52tr, Dan Galic 52tc, 52tr, PCN Photography 1br, 6bl; **DK Images:** Angela Coppola 52b, Mike Garland 86, Ray Moller 67t; **Getty Images:** 1bl, 5, 6t, 10r, 53, 54l, 54c, 54r, 55l, 55r, 64b, 65, 82l, 82r, 86b, AFP 67b, altrendo travel 23, Blake Little 9b, Gallo Images – Aubrey Jonsson 27bl, PhotoAlto / Eric Audras 27tr, Tay Rees 86t, technotr 27br; **MIXA Co., Ltd:** 6br; **Shutterstock.com:** Fotokostic 69b, Rob Wilson 1tr, Stefan Holm 55c; **SuperStock:** Cultura Limited 51b; **Veer / Corbis:** and.one 27tl, jcpjr 33, mindof 1tl, 10l, 70t, mindof 1tl, 10l, 70t, moodboard Photography 64t, Petro Feketa 69t, q-snap 3t, 51t, Robert Marmion 51c, .shock 3b, 52tl, 68, william87 9t, wisky 70b; **www.imagesource.com:** Neil Guegan 50
All other images © Pearson Education

Picture Research by: Caitlin Swain

Every effort has been made to trace the copyright holders and we apologise in advance for any unintentional omissions. We would be pleased to insert the appropriate acknowledgement in any subsequent edition of this publication.

A note from the publisher

In order to ensure that this resource offers high-quality support for the associated BTEC qualification, it has been through a review process by the awarding body to confirm that it fully covers the teaching and learning content of the specification or part of a specification at which it is aimed, and demonstrates an appropriate balance between the development of subject skills, knowledge and understanding, in addition to preparation for assessment.

While the publishers have made every attempt to ensure that advice on the qualification and its assessment is accurate, the official specification and associated assessment guidance materials are the only authoritative source of information and should always be referred to for definitive guidance.

BTEC examiners have not contributed to any sections in this resource relevant to examination papers for which they have responsibility.

No material from an endorsed book will be used verbatim in any assessment set by BTEC.

Endorsement of a book does not mean that the book is required to achieve this BTEC qualification, nor does it mean that it is the only suitable material available to support the qualification, and any resource lists produced by the awarding body shall include this and other appropriate resources.

Contents

This book covers the externally assessed units in the BTEC Level 1/Level 2 First in Sport qualification.

Pearson publishes Sample Assessment Material and the Specification on its website. That is the official content, and this book should be used in conjunction with it. The questions in this book have been written to help you practise what you have learned in your revision. Remember: the real test questions may not look like this.

 Guided These questions provide part of a model answer to help you get started.

Aerobic endurance

1 Three of the following are alternative names for aerobic endurance. Identify the term that is **not**. Put a cross in the box next to the correct answer. **(1 mark)**

A ☐ Cardiorespiratory fitness   **B** ☐ Aerobic fitness

C ☐ Cardiovascular fitness   **D** ☐ Cardiorespiratory endurance

2 Look at the photos of athletes.

(a) Identify which athlete requires the highest level of aerobic endurance. Put a cross in the box by the correct one. **(1 mark)**

A ☐ 100 m sprinter

B ☐ Marathon runner

C ☐ Gymnast

D ☐ Weightlifter

(b) Explain why aerobic endurance is most important to the athlete you selected in your answer to **(a)**. **(2 marks)**

....

....

Guided **3** Complete the following statement about aerobic endurance, using the words from the box below. **(4 marks)**

Aerobic endurance is the ability of the .... system to work efficiently,

supplying oxygen and nutrients to working muscles during sustained physical activity. It is also

responsible for the removal of waste products such as .... and water.

| carbon dioxide | nutrients | oxygen | cardiovascular |

Muscular endurance

1   Which **one** of these statements best describes muscular endurance?
Put a cross in the box next to the correct answer.   **(1 mark)**

A ☐ The ability to use voluntary muscles repeatedly over time without them getting tired

B ☐ The maximum force that can be generated by a muscle or group of muscles

C ☐ The ability to lift a heavy weight quickly

D ☐ The ability to perform strength exercises without fatigue

Guided 2   Muscular endurance is an important component of fitness for many sports performers.

Complete the table below to describe how muscular endurance is used by each performer.
(3 marks)

Performer	How muscular endurance is used in their sport
Rower	Excellent muscular endurance in the upper body and arms allows the rower to row repeatedly against the resistance of the water without tiring.
Marathon runner	
Long-distance swimmer	

3   For each athlete, tick the box to say whether they are using muscular strength or muscular endurance.   **(4 marks)**

	Muscular strength	Muscular endurance
A Cross-country runner	☐	☐
B Shot-putter	☐	☐
C Weightlifter	☐	☐
D Long-distance cyclist	☐	☐

Flexibility

1   Flexibility is important in many activities.

> Below is an incomplete definition of flexibility. Complete the definition by selecting the
> correct word from the box below.   **(1 mark)**

Flexibility is the range of motion possible at a ....

| tendon | muscle | joint | ligament |

> In your online test, you might
> have to drag and drop the
> correct word into the space.

⟩ **Guided** ⟩   2   The images show two different performers: a high jumper and a hurdler.

> Describe how each of these performers needs flexibility to be successful in their activities.
> **(4 marks)**

High jumpers require excellent flexibility in the .... ,

.... and .... to ensure that they are

able to bend their torso and legs around the bar and avoid
knocking it off.

....

....

....

....

3

> Explain why a 100 m sprinter would require high levels of flexibility to perform well in
> their sport.   **(2 marks)**

....

....

....

Speed

1 What is the usual unit of measurement for speed? Put a cross in the box next to the correct answer. **(1 mark)**

A ☐ m/s

B ☐ km/m^2

C ☐ n

D ☐ km/h

2 Complete the following statements about speed. **(3 marks)**

Speed can be defined as .... travelled .... by the time taken.

There are three basic types of speed.

They are .... speed, pure speed and speed endurance.

3 Draw a line between the type of speed and its correct definition. **(3 marks)**

Accelerative speed   Sprints with short recovery periods in-between

Pure speed   Sprints up to 60 metres

Speed endurance   Sprints up to 30 metres

> **Guided**

4 Speed is an important component of fitness for many performers.

Complete the table below to show which type of speed is most important to each of the performers and then describe when the performer would use this type of speed. **(6 marks)**

Performer	Type of speed	When it is used
100 m sprinter	Pure speed	
Long jumper		During the run-up so that they are travelling at maximum speed on take-off.
Hockey player		

Muscular strength

1 | Complete the following sentence using the correct word from the box below. **(1 mark)** |

Muscular strength is an example of .... fitness.

| personal   physical   skill   sport-specific |

2 | Complete the following statement describing the relationship between muscular strength and power. **(1 mark)** |

Power is the ability to use muscular strength at ....

| Try to remember the calculation for power:
    power = muscular strength × speed
Once you can remember this you will be able to describe the relationship. |

Guided **3** The athlete in the image is taking part in a shot put competition.

| Explain the importance of muscular strength in shot put. **(2 marks)** |

In shot put, muscular strength is needed to maximise the distance travelled. ....

....

....

Agility

1 Agility is an important aspect of many team sports.

> Select the correct words from the box below to complete the definition of agility.   **(2 marks)**

Agility is the ability to make a controlled .... of direction at ....

speed	improvement	change	will

2 The image below shows competitors in a netball match.

> Explain how a netball player uses agility in her sport.   **(2 marks)**

....

....

....

3 Look at the images below of competitors running in two events.

> **(a)** State whether the competitors in event A or B have a greater need for agility.
> Put a cross in the correct box.   **(1 mark)**

A ☐

B ☐

> **Guided**   **(b)** Explain why the athletes in the event you selected in your answer to **(a)** have a greater need for agility.   **(2 marks)**

The competitors in .... need agility for .... the .... The

competitors in .... do not have as much need for agility because they are running

in a straight line with nothing in their way.

Balance

1   Which **one** of the following is a type of balance? Put a cross in the box next to the correct answer. **(1 mark)**

A ☐ Static

B ☐ Moving

C ☐ Alternating

D ☐ Held

Guided   **2**   Outline the differences between static and dynamic balance, using examples. **(4 marks)**

Static balance is the ability to maintain the centre of gravity over a stationary base of

support. An example of this would be ....

Dynamic balance is about a performer's ability to ....

.... An example of this would be a gymnast performing a

cartwheel.

3   Give **two** examples of how balance is important in sporting activities. **(2 marks)**

....

....

....

....

4   Give **one** example of a player in netball who requires good balance. **(1 mark)**

....

....

Coordination

1
> Which **one** of the following is the correct definition of coordination?
> Put a cross in the box next to the correct answer.   **(1 mark)**

A ☐ The ability to work well as part of a team

B ☐ The ability to use two or more body parts together

C ☐ The ability to respond quickly to a stimulus

D ☐ The ability to use different aspects of fitness at the same time

▷ **Guided** ▷ 2 Many sports require excellent hand–eye coordination, foot–eye coordination or hand–to–hand coordination.

> Draw lines to match the sports below with the correct type of coordination needed. **(3 marks)**

Tennis   Foot–eye coordination

Football   Hand–to–hand coordination

Basketball   Hand–eye coordination

3 Cricket is a sport in which coordination is important.

> Give **two** examples to show how a cricket player would use coordination in their sport.
>   **(2 marks)**

....

....

....

....

....

....

> Think about ways in which the batters or fielders might need to be coordinated.

Power

1
> Complete the equation below to show how power is calculated. **(1 mark)**

Power = ... × ....

> **Guided**

2 The images show two sports performers engaging in two physical activities: tennis and rugby.

> Using an example for each, explain how each performer would use power in their performance. **(4 marks)**

The tennis player needs power in order to make fast shots that are harder to return.

Increased power means the opposition has less time to respond.

....
....

3
> Explain the impact of power on the performance of a javelin thrower. **(2 marks)**

....
....
....

Reaction time

> **Guided** **1**

Complete the following statement about reaction time, using the correct words from the box below. **(2 marks)**

Reaction time is the time taken for a sports performer to respond to a stimulus and the initiation of this ....

time	stimulus	response	reaction

2 Look at the images below.

(a) Which type of sports performer – A or B – would benefit most from having a good reaction time? Put a cross in the box next to the correct answer. **(1 mark)**

A ☐ Sprinter

B ☐ Shot-putter

(b) Explain the reasons for your choice of answer in **(a)**. **(2 marks)**

....

....

....

....

The importance of fitness components for success in sport

1

Which **one** of the following aspects of fitness would be the most useful to a long-distance swimmer?
Put a cross in the box next to the correct answer.   **(1 mark)**

A ☐ Agility   **B** ☐ Muscular endurance in the upper arms

C ☐ Reaction time   **D** ☐ Balance

2

State **one** reason why agility is a useful fitness component for a rugby player.   **(1 mark)**

....

Imagine watching rugby live or on the television – what aspects of fitness can you see the players using?

Guided   **3**   Below is a table of different sports performers.

(a) Identify the components of fitness needed by each performer.   **(3 marks)**

(b) For each performer, state why they need that component for their sport.   **(3 marks)**

Sports example	Aspect of fitness that is important	Why it is important
Gymnast		It allows them to move their joints through a large range of movement and hold more extreme body positions.
Discus thrower	Balance	
Football goalkeeper		It helps them respond quickly to shots on goal.

4   Explain why the fitness requirements of a football striker and goalkeeper would be different.
                                                                         (4 marks)

....

....

....

....

Exercise intensity: heart rate

1   Define the term 'heart rate'.   **(1 mark)**

....

Guided   **2**   Yosef is a 23-year-old athlete.

Calculate his maximum heart rate in bpm, showing your workings.   **(2 marks)**

Maximum heart rate = 220 − ....

In the online test you will be given a box to show your workings.

....

3   What does 'bpm' stand for?   **(1 mark)**

....

4   Explain why it is important to be able to work out your maximum heart rate.   **(2 marks)**

....

....

....

....

Exercise intensity: the Borg (RPE) scale

1 │ What does 'RPE' stand for? **(1 mark)**

....

2 │ Circle the rating on the scale below that would suggest exercise is being performed at a moderate intensity. **(1 mark)**

Rating of Perceived Exertion	Intensity
6	No exertion
7	
8	
9	
10	
11	
12	
13	
14	
15	
16	
17	
18	
19	
20	

> **Guided** 3 │ State **two** benefits of using this scale to measure RPE. **(2 marks)**

1   The Borg (RPE) scale can be used to estimate heart rate and as a tool for calculating training zones.

2   ....

....

Exercise intensity: training zones

1 If you are trying to improve aerobic endurance, what training zone would it be most appropriate to work in? Put a cross in the box next to the correct answer. **(1 mark)**

A ☐ 35–40% of HRmax

B ☐ 40–50% of HRmax

C ☐ 50–60% of HRmax

D ☐ 60–85% of HRmax

> In the online test, you might be asked to select from a dropdown list.

2 Explain why it might **not** be appropriate for a 100 m sprinter to train within their aerobic training zone? **(2 marks)**

....

....

....

....

Guided **3** Mohammed is 36 years old.

Calculate his target heart rate zone for improving his aerobic endurance. Show your workings. **(4 marks)**

220 – 36 (age) = 184

60% of 184 = 110

85% of 184 = ...

Therefore the heart rate zone is between 110– .... bpm.

> Remember to work out the percentage you need to complete the following calculations:
> $60 \times 184 \div 100$
> and
> $85 \times 184 \div 100$

Basic principles of training

1 What does the acronym FITT stand for? Fill in the missing word below.   **(1 mark)**

F: Frequency

I: Intensity

T: ....

T: Type

2 Which part of the FITT principle do the following statements represent?   **(4 marks)**

A Training more often each week   ....

B Training for longer each week   ....

C Lifting heavier weights each week   ....

D Selecting a specific training method   ....

Guided **3** Naseem is a swimmer and is planning a training programme to improve her aerobic endurance.

Using the FITT principle, describe **three** ways in which Naseem could adjust her training as she progresses.   **(3 marks)**

Naseem could adjust her training by:

(a) using training aids to add resistance and increase intensity

(b) ....

....

(c) ....

> Think about how training can be made harder over time.

Additional principles of training 1

1   Which principle of training must be applied to ensure training matches the needs of an individual's sport? Put a cross in the box next to the correct answer.   **(1 mark)**

A ☐ Overload

B ☐ Intensity

C ☐ Specificity

D ☐ Reversibility

▷ Guided ▷   2   Explain **one** reason why fartlek training would be an appropriate training method for a football player.   **(2 marks)**

Make sure you reference the football player specifically.

Fartlek training would be appropriate for a football player because the training is varied in

pace. This ....

No footballer runs continuously for 90 minutes so periods of .... followed by

periods of .... are most similar to the requirements of the game.

3   Abby is a long-distance swimmer. She is planning a training programme to help her prepare for an event.

   (a) Explain why Abby should train in the pool rather than on a track.   **(2 marks)**

   ....

   ....

   ....

   Abby trains using weights as well as her training in the pool.

   (b) Explain how this training still meets the needs of specificity.   **(2 marks)**

   ....

   ....

   ....

Additonal principles of training 2

1

> Give **one** reason why it is important that overload is applied gradually over time.   **(1 mark)**

....

Guided   **2**

> State **two** ways in which progressive overload could be applied to a six-week training programme and for **each** way give an example of it in practice.   **(4 marks)**

> This question requires you to remember the acronym FITT.

1   Increase the frequency of training – for example, ...

....

2   ....

....

3   Sarah took part in a 12-week training programme to improve her aerobic endurance. She did the multistage fitness test at the start, in the middle and at the end of her programme.

Sarah's results	
Bleep 1	6.3
Bleep 2	7.1
Bleep 3	7.1

> Describe what her results tell you about the way she used progressive overload.   **(2 marks)**

....

....

....

....

....

....

Additional principles of training 3

1

> Which **one** of the following statements best describes the principle of individual differences/needs in training? Put a cross in the box next to the correct answer. **(1 mark)**

   A ☐ Making the body work harder over time by increasing the length of the training sessions

   B ☐ Not training when you are injured or fatigued

   C ☐ Designing a programme to meet the training needs and goals of the individual

   D ☐ Ensuring that the individual knows the aim of the fitness training programme

2   Danuta is a 100 m runner and Edward is a marathon runner.

> Explain why Danuta and Edward should have different training programmes. **(2 marks)**

....

....

....

....

3

> **(a)** What type of training would be most appropriate for Danuta to follow? **(1 mark)**

....

....

> **(b)** What type of training would be most appropriate for Edward to follow? **(1 mark)**

....

....

Additonal principles of training 4

1 | Define the principle of 'reversibility'. | (1 mark) |

....

....

2 | Give **one** reason why rest is an important part of the training schedule. | (1 mark) |

....

3 | Look at the training data below. Which athlete has been affected by reversibility? | (1 mark) |

	Week 1	Week 2	Week 3	Week 4	Week 5
Prakash	60 mins	57 mins	55 mins	54 mins	51 mins
Elena	55 mins	54 mins	52 mins	49 mins	48 mins
Kim	49 mins	47 mins	43 mins	44 mins	46 mins

....

4 | State **one** factor that could lead to reversibility in an athlete's training. | (1 mark) |

....

Additonal principles of training 5

Guided 1

Which **one** of the following examples of variation would be most appropriate for a badminton player? Put a cross in the box next to the correct answer. **(1 mark)**

A ☒ Court work; strength work in the gym; weights for muscular endurance

B ☐ Pool work for muscular endurance; gym work for power; continuous training on the track

C ☐ Fartlek training in the park; gym work for general fitness; court work

D ☐ Court work; cardiovascular work in the pool; flexibility work in the conditioning room

2

Give **one** example of why variation in training is important. **(1 mark)**

Think about why you vary your own training routines.

....

3 Rivka does continuous training regularly.

Give **one** example of how she could add variation to her training. **(1 mark)**

....

4 Lucy is taking part in a training programme to improve her base levels of fitness.

Describe how she can use variation to reduce the chance of boredom in her training. **(4 marks)**

....

....

....

....

....

....

Think about the other types of training that you've learned about in this unit and always remember to apply the FITT principle.

Circuit training

Look at the training circuit to the right and answer the questions that follow.

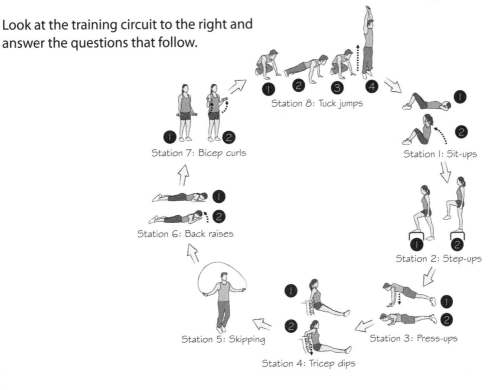

Station 8: Tuck jumps

Station 7: Bicep curls

Station 6: Back raises

Station 5: Skipping

Station 4: Tricep dips

Station 3: Press-ups

Station 2: Step-ups

Station 1: Sit-ups

1 Which stations would help to develop the following aspects of fitness?   **(3 marks)**

A Muscular endurance in the abdominals = station

B Quadriceps power = station

C Aerobic endurance = station

2 Describe **two** ways in which exercise intensity could be increased on this circuit.   **(4 marks)**

....

....

....

....

> You need to think about the FITT principle here and how you can apply it to your answer.

Guided **3** Sofia has designed her own training circuit. She has press-ups at station 3 and bicep curls at station 4.

Explain the problem with Sofia's training circuit and give **one** suggestion for improvement.
    (3 marks)

Stations 3 and 4 both exercise the same body part. This is a problem because of the risk of

fatigue and injury. There needs to be some recovery time between each station. The circuit

could be improved by ....

....

Continuous training

1
> Which aspect of fitness is most commonly improved through continuous training?   **(1 mark)**

....

2
> Identify **two** sports activities in which continuous training would be suitable for sports performers wishing to improve their fitness specifically for that sport.   **(2 marks)**

....

....

Guided   **3**   Look at the table below showing heart rate data.

> Fill in the missing gaps to show the correct heart rate data for these athletes if they were working within their aerobic training zone. You may use the box below for your workings.
> **(6 marks)**

Name	Age (years)	HRmax (bpm)	Aerobic zone lower limit (bpm)	Aerobic zone upper limit (bpm)
Di	68	152	91	129
Dave	50	170	102	145
Minsuh	34		112	
Adam	20			170

> Di's HRmax: 220 − 68 = 152
>
> Dave's upper limit: 85 × 170 ÷ 100 = 145

> Remember you should normally round numbers up or down. So if you had 91.2 it would be 91, while 97.7 would be 98.

4
> Identify **one** impact on your fitness of consistently exceeding your upper aerobic training zone?   **(1 mark)**

....

....

Fartlek training

1   Name **one** training aid that can be used in fartlek training to increase intensity.   **(1 mark)**

....

Guided   2   Explain **one** way a tennis player would adapt fartlek training to suit the needs of their sport.   **(2 marks)**

As tennis involves players sprinting short distances in order to reach the ball, training should

involve ....

....

> Think about the movements involved in a game of tennis.

3   Look at the photo, which shows suitable terrain for fartlek training.

Describe the features of this terrain that make it suitable for fartlek training.   **(3 marks)**

....

....

....

Interval training

1 Name **one** key feature of interval training. **(1 mark)**

....

> **Guided**

2 The diagrams below show possible interval training plans.

(a) Which diagram best demonstrates interval training suitable for a 100 m sprinter wishing to improve their speed? Put a cross in the box by the correct answer. **(1 mark)**

Diagram A   Diagram B

Work   Rest   Work   Rest   Work Rest Work Rest Work Rest

☐   ☐

(b) Explain the reasons for your choice. **(2 marks)**

Diagram .... best represents the interval training

most suitable for a sprinter. To improve speed, the best

intervals need to be ....

> Think about the nature of the event and try to link this to your answer.

....

3 Identify **one** purpose of rest periods in interval training. **(1 mark)**

....

Plyometric training

1

Which **one** of the following exercises would be most suitable in plyometric training?
Put a cross in the box next to the correct answer. **(1 mark)**

A ☐ Tricep dips

B ☐ Sit-ups

C ☐ Hurdle jumps

D ☐ Shuttle runs

Guided **2**

What happens to the working muscles during a plyometric exercise such as lunging? **(1 mark)**

Muscle lengthening immediately followed by ....

3 Laura is a high jumper. She uses plyometric training.

Explain **one** reason why this type of training would be beneficial to her performance. **(2 marks)**

....

....

4

Give **two** disadvantages of plyometric training. **(2 marks)**

....

....

Speed training methods

1. Which **one** of the following is **not** a type of speed training? Put a cross in the box next to the correct answer. **(1 mark)**

    A ☐ Hollow sprints

    B ☐ Sprint intervals

    C ☐ Box sprints

    D ☐ Acceleration sprints

2. Name the type of speed training that is made up of a series of sprints and rest periods, where rest periods may include walking or jogging. **(1 mark)**

    ....

Guided 3. Give **one** example of a sports performer who might use speed interval training and explain why it would be an appropriate choice. **(3 marks)**

    Speed interval training may be used by long-distance runners because ....

    ....

    ....

4. Julian completes the following training routine.

    A standing start

    ↓

    Jogging

    ↓

    Striding

    ↓

    Maximum sprint

    He completes three sets of this routine, walking in-between each set.

    Which of the following techniques is Julian using? Put a cross in the box next to the correct answer. **(1 mark)**

    A ☐ Hollow sprints

    B ☐ Circuit training

    C ☐ Acceleration sprints

    D ☐ Sprint intervals

Flexibility training

Guided 1 | Describe the difference between active and passive stretching. **(2 marks)** |

Active stretching is performed without .... and relies on internal forces to stretch the muscle. Passive stretching uses another .... or .... to provide resistance.

2 | State **one** benefit of including some sort of stretching in your warm-up routine. **(1 mark)** |

....

3 | Insert the **two** missing words to complete the name of a type of stretching. **(1 mark)** |

.... facilitation

> Remember that facilitation means helping something to happen.

4 The images below show different kinds of stretches.

| Match the image with the correct description. **(4 marks)** |

Passive ☐   PNF ☐   Ballistic ☐   Active ☐

A

B

C

D

27

Weight training

1 State **two** components of fitness that weight training helps to develop.   **(2 marks)**

....

....

Guided **2** Explain the difference between repetitions and sets.   **(2 marks)**

Repetitions are the number of times a weightlifting exercise ....,

for example, 12 reps. Sets are ....,

for example, 3 sets of 12 reps.

3 An athlete is training at 90 per cent of their 1RM.

Which type of strength is this helping to build?   **(1 mark)**

....

4 Give **one** example of a sports performer who would benefit from weight training.   **(1 mark)**

....

5 Outline what happens to the load-to-weight ratio when you compare training for strength endurance with training for maximum strength at 75% 1RM.   **(4 marks)**

....

....

....

....

Fitness testing: importance to sports performers and coaches

1 Baseline scores from fitness tests are important as they give a set of data to compare future scores against.

> Give **another** reason why the collection of baseline data is important. **(1 mark)**

....

Guided 2 Fitness testing can provide benefits for sports performers and coaches.

> Describe **one** possible benefit of fitness testing to a coach and **one** benefit to a sports performer. **(4 marks)**

> Make sure you describe **two** different benefits.

Benefit of fitness testing to a **coach**:

....

....

Benefit of fitness testing to a **performer**:

It can be motivating because the performer can see how much they are improving as a result

of their training over time.

3 The table below shows the results of three fitness tests taken by an individual before and after a training programme.

Fitness test	Pre-training	Post-training
35 m sprint test	5.1 s	4.6 s
1 min press-up test	13 press-ups	29 press-ups
Sit and reach test	8.8 cm	6.8 cm

> Use the data in the table to interpret whether the training programme has been successful in terms of improving:
>
> **(a)** upper body muscular endurance. **(1 mark)**

....

> **(b)** hamstring flexibility. **(1 mark)**

....

Fitness testing: issues, validity and reliability

1 Reliability and validity mean two different things.

> Match the correct definition to each term.   **(2 marks)**

Reliability   The ability to repeatedly carry out a test and get the same result each time.

Validity   How accurate a test is so that it measures what it should measure.

2
> When conducting a fitness test who do you need to gather informed consent from?   **(1 mark)**

....

Guided   **3**
> Give **three** examples of factors that may influence the reliability of a fitness test.   **(3 marks)**

    1   Length and type of warm-up

    2   ....

    3   ....

4
> Using an example, explain **one** reason why calibration is important for ensuring validity.   **(2 marks)**

....

....

....

....

Fitness tests: skinfold testing (body composition 1)

1   Which **one** of the following contains the correct locations for taking female skinfold measurements? **(1 mark)**

   A ☐ Chest, abdomen and thigh   **B** ☐ Chest, suprailiac and thigh

   C ☐ Tricep, suprailiac and thigh   **D** ☐ Tricep, abdomen and calf

2   Name the instrument used to take skinfold measurements. **(1 mark)**

....

Guided   **3**   Using the Jackson-Pollock (J-P) nomogram below, complete the following table. **(3 marks)**

If Isaac is 15 years old and the sum of his skinfolds is 40, his total body fat is 11 per cent. To find this out, join the age of the person to the sum of their skinfolds using a straight line. You can then see their total body fat where it crosses the line in the middle.

Name	Age (years)	Skinfold total (mm)	Body fat percentage (%)
Chloe (female)	18	55	
Ayesha (female)	26	25	12
Charlie (male)	15	120	

Rating	Males	Females
Very low	<7	<13
Slim	7–12	13–20
Ideal	13–17	21–25
Overweight	18–28	26–32
Obese	29+	33+

4   Explain which of the subjects in Question 3 has the most concerning level of body fat and why. **(4 marks)**

....

....

....

....

Fitness tests:
BMI (body composition 2)

Guided ▷ **1**

> What does 'BMI' stand for? **(1 mark)**

Body .... index

2

> What is the unit of measurement for BMI? Put a cross in the box next to the correct answer.
> **(1 mark)**

A ☐ mg/m^2 B ☐ kg/cm^2

C ☐ kg/m^2 D ☐ g/cm^2

3

> Using a sports example, explain **one** reason why BMI is not always an accurate method of measuring body composition. **(2 marks)**

....

....

4 Jakob is 1.5 m tall and weighs 66 kg. The formula to calculate BMI is:

$$\frac{\text{Body weight (kg)}}{\text{Height (m)} \times \text{Height (m)}}$$

> **(a)** Work out Jakob's BMI, using the usual unit of measurement. **(2 marks)**

....

> **(b)** Using the table provided, how would you classify Jacob's weight from his BMI? **(1 mark)**

Rating	BMI
Underweight	≤19
Desirable	20–25
Overweight	26–30
Obese	31+

....

....

Fitness tests: bioelectrical impedance analysis (body composition 3)

1 The images below show two different tests for measuring body fat percentage.

> Identify the **one** showing bioelectrical impedance analysis. **(1 mark)**

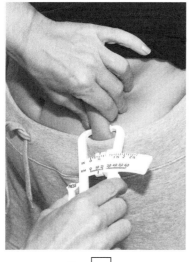

A ☐

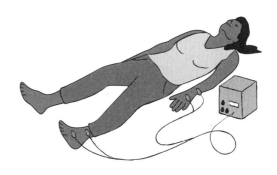

B ☐

Guided **2**

> Give **two** disadvantages of bioelectrical impedance analysis as a testing method. **(2 marks)**

1   The equipment is very specialised and therefore expensive.

2   ....

3

> Identify the impact of dehydration on the results of this test. **(1 mark)**

....

....

4

> Which **one** of the following provides the greatest resistance to the electrical current?
> Put a cross in the box next to the correct answer. **(1 mark)**

A ☐ Body fat

B ☐ Fat-free mass

C ☐ Muscle

D ☐ Bone

Fitness tests: muscular endurance – abdominal

Look at the image below and answer the questions.

1
> Name the test shown in the image. **(1 mark)**

....

2
> Which **one** of the following is the usual unit of measurement for the test shown in the image? **(1 mark)**

A ☐ kg/m^2

B ☐   reps/minute

C ☐   second (s)

D ☐   kgm/s

Guided **3**
> Describe the method for the test shown in the image. **(3 marks)**

Step 1:   Lie on the mat with your knees bent and your feet flat on the floor.

Step 2:   ....

Step 3:   ....

4
> Give **two** examples of sporting activities in which participants would be expected to score highly in the test shown in the image. **(2 marks)**

....

....

Fitness tests: muscular endurance – upper body

Look at the image below and answer the questions.

1 Name the test shown in the image. **(1 mark)**

....

2 Describe the method for the test shown in the image. **(3 marks)**

Step 1: ....

Step 2: ....

Step 3: ....

⟩ Guided ⟩ 3 Describe the difference between the standard and modified test method for the test shown in the image. **(2 marks)**

In the standard test, the subject takes all of their weight on their

hands and feet. In the modified version ....

> The image shows the standard test.

....

4 Identify why the test shown in the image is **not** a measure of muscular endurance in the legs. **(1 mark)**

....

....

Fitness tests: speed – 35 m sprint test

Guided 1

> Give **three** examples of sports performers who would benefit from using the 35 m sprint test.   **(3 marks)**

A hurdler, a centre court netball player and a ....

2

> Which **two** of the following could influence the reliability of the 35 m sprint test? Put a cross in the box next to the correct answer.   **(2 marks)**

A ☐ Not using a tape measure to mark out 35 m in one test

B ☐ Doing both tests indoors

C ☐ Doing the tests at different times of the day

D ☐ Having an audience for both tests

E ☐ Using the same equipment in both tests

3   The 35 m sprint test is normally conducted three times.

> Which of these results is taken as the performer's final result?   **(1 mark)**

....

....

4

> Identify **one** way in which the 35 m sprint test is different from the Illinois agility run test.   **(1 mark)**

....

....

Fitness tests: MSFT (aerobic endurance 1)

1 Define 'VO^2 max' and give its usual unit of measurement. **(2 marks)**

....

....

2 What does 'MSFT' stand for? **(1 mark)**

....

Guided **3** Using **three** examples, identify when an athlete should finish their participation in the MSFT. **(3 marks)**

An athlete should finish this test when they are either no longer physically able to keep up

with the beeps, when ....

or when ....

4 A lacrosse team wants to carry out fitness testing to test aerobic endurance.

Give **one** reason why a lacrosse team may choose to use the MSFT instead of another type of test. **(1 mark)**

....

....

5 Give **two** factors which may influence the reliability of MSFT results. **(2 marks)**

....

....

Fitness tests: forestry step test (aerobic endurance 2)

1 What is the role of the metronome in the forestry step test? **(1 mark)**

> Remember a metronome is a device that produces regular beats. Think about what that noise could help you to do.

....

....

2 Give **one** disadvantage of using the forestry step test as a measure of aerobic endurance. **(1 mark)**

....

....

Guided **3** Describe the method for the forestry step test. **(5 marks)**

> Remember that another term for method is protocol. You may see this in your test.

Step 1: Record body weight with clothing on.

Step 2: ....

Step 3: ....

Step 4: ....

Step 5: Fifteen seconds after stopping, count your pulse for 15 seconds and record this number.

Fitness tests: agility

1   Which fitness test is shown in the image? Put a cross in the box next to the correct answer.

(1 mark)

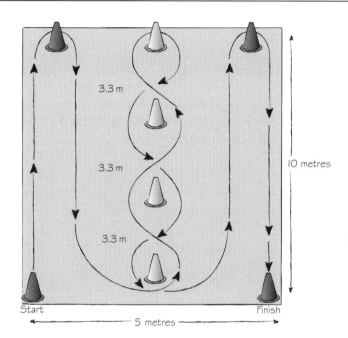

A ☐   35 m sprint test   B ☐   Multistage fitness test

C ☐   Forestry step test   D ☐   Illinois agility run test

2   Give **two** examples of sports performers who may choose to use the test shown in the picture to monitor the effectiveness of their training programmes.   **(2 marks)**

1 ....

2 ....

⟩ **Guided** ⟩ **3**   Give **one** advantage and **one** disadvantage of the Illinois agility run test.   **(2 marks)**

Advantage: It requires minimal amounts of ....

Disadvantage: ....

4   Identify **one** reason why the Illinois agility run test would be a valid test for a tennis player.

(1 mark)

....

Fitness tests: vertical jump test (anaerobic power)

Guided **1**

> What does the vertical jump test measure? **(1 mark)**

Anaerobic power in the ....

2

> Which **one** of the following is the unit of measurement for the vertical jump test? Put a cross in the box next to the correct answer. **(1 mark)**

A ☐ lbs/min

B ☐ lbs/s

C ☐ kgm/m

D ☐ kgm/s

3

> Give **one** example of a sports performer who should score highly in this test and briefly explain your reasoning. **(2 marks)**

....

....

4

> What type of training could be used to improve results on the vertical jump test? **(1 mark)**

....

Fitness tests: grip dynamometer (strength)

1   Which of the following is **not** an advantage of the grip dynamometer test? Put a cross in the box next to the correct answer. **(1 mark)**

A ☐   It can be conducted anywhere

B ☐   It is easy to carry out

C ☐   It needs specialised equipment

D ☐   It is quick to carry out

Guided

2   Rachel takes the grip strength test 3 times; twice with her right hand and once with her left. She then takes an average of her three scores.

Identify **one** problem with this result. **(1 mark)**

It would not be accurate because the three readings were not taken with ....

> Think about the terms reliability and validity when answering this question.

3   Noah is a weightlifter and wants to measure his leg strength in order to plan a fitness training programme. He plans to use the grip dynamometer test.

Explain why the grip dynamometer test would not be a valid test for Noah to use. **(2 marks)**

....

....

4   Which **one** of the following sports performers would most benefit from using the grip dynamometer test? Put a cross in the box next to the correct answer. **(1 mark)**

A ☐   Football striker

B ☐   Long jumper

C ☐   Judo player

D ☐   Swimmer

Fitness tests: flexibility

Look at the image below and answer the questions.

1   Which **one** of the following is the test shown in the image above? Put a cross in the box next to the correct answer. **(1 mark)**

A ☐ Toe touch test

B ☐ Sit and reach test

C ☐ Lumbar flex test

D ☐ Sit and stretch test

2   Name **one** sporting activity that you may be training for if you used the test shown in the image. **(1 mark)**

....

Guided **3**   Give **two** disadvantages of the test shown in the image. **(2 marks)**

1   Variations in trunk and arm length can make comparisons difficult.

2   ....

4   Name **one** specific type of training that would help to improve the scores obtained on this test. **(1 mark)**

....

....

Exam skills 1

For each question, choose an answer A, B, C or D and put a cross in the box next to the correct answer.

1 Which **one** of the following is **not** part of the FITT principle? **(1 mark)**

A ☐ Intensity   B ☐ Frequency

C ☐ Total   D ☐ Time

2 Which **one** of the following statements about training is **not** true? **(1 mark)**

A ☐ Hollow sprints are a type of speed training

B ☐ 100 m sprinters often use continuous training

C ☐ Fartlek training is good for games players

D ☐ Interval training is beneficial to a hockey player

> This question tells you that three of the statements are true and one is not true. You have to find the one that is not true.

3 Which **one** of the following is the formula for calculating maximum heart rate? **(1 mark)**

A ☐ HRmax = 250 − age   B ☐ HRmax = 220 + bpm

C ☐ HRmax = 220 − age   D ☐ HRmax = 300 ÷ height (m)

4 Which **one** of the following can be used to calculate body fat percentage? **(1 mark)**

A ☐ The Jackson-Pollock nomogram   B ☐ The Borg (RPE) scale

C ☐ The forestry test   D ☐ RPE

5 Which **one** of the following is **not** an example of a type of stretching used to increase flexibility? **(1 mark)**

A ☐ Passive   B ☐ PNF

C ☐ Ballistic   D ☐ Bounce

6 Which **one** of the following definitions best describes the term validity? **(1 mark)**

A ☐ Being able to repeat a test reliably each time

B ☐ Measuring what you actually say you are measuring

C ☐ Changing the environment within which a test is taken

D ☐ Using the correct name and method for the test

Exam skills 2

1

> Name **one** appropriate fitness test to measure agility and describe how it is carried out.
>
> **(3 marks)**

Test: ....

Method: ....

....

....

2 Molly is 17 years old.

> What are the upper and lower limits of her aerobic training zone? Show your workings in the box below.   **(2 marks)**

....

3 When planning her training, Alba applied the principle of progressive overload by altering the time spent training.

> Explain why this will help Alba improve her fitness.   **(2 marks)**

....

....

....

4

> Give a definition of 'coordination' and then explain **two** reasons why it is important to a tennis player.   **(4 marks)**

Definition: ....

Why it is important: ....

....

....

....

Exam skills 3

You need to be able to identify exactly what the question is asking you to do.

1

> State an appropriate fitness test for the following aspects of fitness.   **(3 marks)**

> **State** – give one clear answer, normally just one piece of information.

A Agility: ....

B Hamstring flexibility: ....

C Aerobic endurance: ....

3

> Compare the protocol for the Illinois agility run test and the 35 m sprint test, considering which test may be a more valid measure of sprint speed for a rugby player   **(2 marks)**

....

....

....

....

> **Compare** – look at two things you are being asked to compare and say how they are similar and how they are different.

3

> Using your knowledge of training, interpret the data in the table below, commenting on the effectiveness of each athlete's training.   **(8 marks)**

Name	MSFT test 1	MSFT test 2	MSFT test 3
Lin	4.4	5.3	7.1
Richard	5.5	5.6	5.5
Pedro	6.1	6.8	4.5

> **Interpret** – look critically at the data provided and draw a reasonable conclusion.

....

....

....

....

....

....

....

Major voluntary muscles 1

Guided   **1**   The images below highlight different muscles.

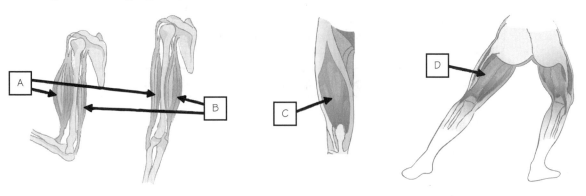

> **(a)** Name muscles **A**, **B**, **C** and **D** in the images.   **(4 marks)**

> **(b)** Explain the role of each muscle.   **(8 marks)**

Muscle A

Name: Biceps

Role: Flexion of the arm at the elbow joint

Muscle B

Name: ....

Role: ....

Muscle C

Name: ....

Role: ....

Muscle D

Name: ....

Role: ....

Major voluntary muscles 2

1   What is the name of the muscle highlighted in **Figure 1**?   **(1 mark)**

Figure 1

....

2   The role of the above muscle is shoulder elevation.

Provide **one** example of a sporting movement that requires the contraction of this muscle.
(1 mark)

....

....

Guided   3   What is the name of the muscle shown in **Figure 2** and what is its role?   **(2 marks)**

Figure 2

......................: adducts the arm at the ....

....

4   Provide **one** example of a sporting movement that requires the contraction of the above muscle.   **(1 mark)**

....

....

Had a go ☐ Nearly there ☐ Nailed it! ☐

Major voluntary muscles 3

Guided

1 What is the name of the muscle highlighted in **Figure 1** below? **(1 mark)**

Figure 1

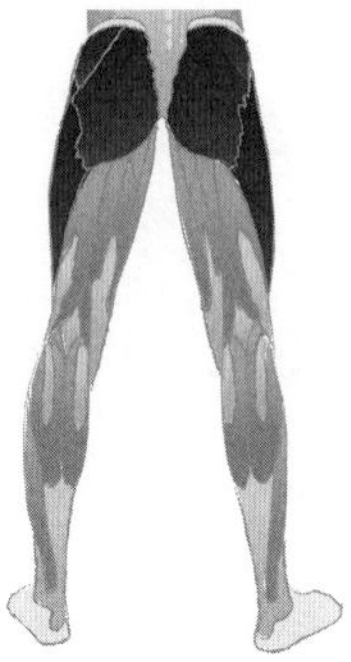

Gluteus ....

2 Which **one** of the following best describes the role of the muscle in **Figure 1**? **(1 mark)**

A ☐ Flex the hip

B ☐ Extend the hip

C ☐ Flex the knee

D ☐ Extend the knee

3 Name the muscle that is highlighted in **Figure 2**. **(1 mark)**

Figure 2

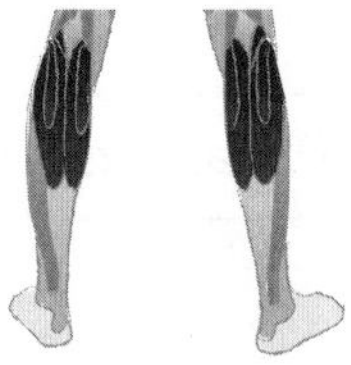

....

4 Provide **one** example of a sporting movement/gym movement that requires the contraction of the muscle in **Figure 2**. **(1 mark)**

....

5 Name the muscle highlighted in **Figure 3**. **(1 mark)**

Figure 3

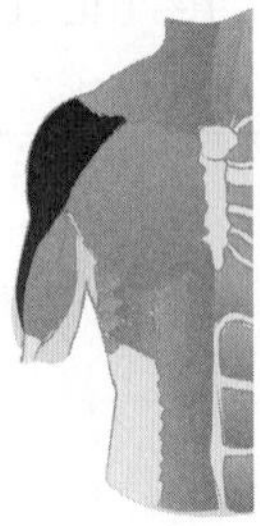

....

6 Which **one** of the following best describes the role of the muscle in **Figure 3**? **(1 mark)**

A ☐ Adducts the shoulder

B ☐ Abducts the elbow

C ☐ Abducts the shoulder

D ☐ Adducts the elbow

Types of muscle

1   Complete columns two and three of the table for voluntary and involuntary muscle.   **(4 marks)**

Type of muscle	Location	Characteristics
Voluntary	•	• Conscious control •
Involuntary	• Stomach •	• Slow, rhythmic contraction •

2   Fill in the blanks to complete the following statements.   **(4 marks)**

(a) Voluntary muscle is also known as .... or .... muscle.

(b) Involuntary muscle is also known as .... or .... muscle.

3   Fill in the blanks to complete the following statements.   **(3 marks)**

(a) Heart muscle is also known as ....

(b) Heart muscle is under .... control because it needs to keep ....
to keep us alive.

4   Which **one** of the following statements is true? Put a cross in the box next to the correct
answer.   **(1 mark)**

A ☐   Cardiac muscles can be found in several locations in the body

B ☐   Skeletal muscle is not under our conscious control

C ☐   Cardiac muscle can only be found in the heart

D ☐   Skeletal muscle can be found in the walls of blood vessels

5   Which **one** of the following is a characteristic of cardiac muscle? Put a cross in the box next to
the correct answer.   **(1 mark)**

A ☐   It is under conscious control

B ☐   Contractions are slow and sustained

C ☐   Contractions are fast and irregular

D ☐   Contractions are rapid and sustained

Voluntary muscle movements

> **Guided**

1 Using the words in the box below, fill in the blanks in the following sentence about antagonistic pairs. **(1 mark)**

joints	movement	together	skeletal

Skeletal muscles work .... to provide .... of the ....

2 Explain how muscles work in antagonistic pairs and provide an appropriate example. **(2 marks)**

....

....

....

3 Circle the correct words in the following sentences. **(2 marks)**

Muscles are connected to bones via **ligaments/tendons/muscle**.

When a muscle contracts, it **pulls/pushes** on a **ligament/tendon/muscle**, which then **pushes/pulls** on the bone to create movement.

4 Look at the image of the football player.

Name the muscles being used in the image. For each muscle, state which muscle is the agonist and which is the antagonist. **(2 marks)**

	Name	**Antagonist/agonist**
A		
B		

5 Look at the image of the footballer again.

Describe how the role of the muscles in the kicking action is reversed when the leg starts to extend through to kick the ball. **(2 marks)**

....

....

Antagonistic muscle pairs

Guided 1 | Draw lines between the matching antagonistic pairs. **(4 marks)**

Biceps		Trapezius
Rectus abdominus		Hamstrings
Pectoralis major		Triceps
Quadriceps		Erector spinae

2 **Figure 1** shows a man performing a high jump.

(a) During take-off which **one** of the following muscles is acting as the agonist at the ankle joint when the ankle is plantarflexing to aid take-off? **(1 mark)**

A ☐ Quadriceps   B ☐ Gastrocneimus

C ☐ Tibialis anterior   D ☐ Hamstrings

(b) During take-off which **one** of the following muscles is the antagonist allowing the ankle to plantarflex and aid take-off? **(1 mark)**

A ☐ Quadriceps B ☐ Gastrocneimus C ☐ Tibialis anterior D ☐ Hamstrings

Figure 1

3 | Name the antagonistic muscle pair that an individual performing the upward phase in a sit-up, as shown in **Figure 2**, would use. **(2 marks)**

....

....

....

....

Figure 2

4 **Figure 3** shows a netball player taking a shot on goal.

Name **two** of the antagonistic muscle pairs that are being actively engaged. **(2 marks)**

....

....

....

....

Figure 3

Types of contraction

Guided 1

For each type of muscle contraction listed in the table, describe what happens and give an example related to sport. **(6 marks)**

Type of muscle contraction	Description	Example
Concentric		Biceps: when lifting a weight during a bicep curl
Eccentric		
Isometric	When a muscle contracts but does not shorten and there is no movement	

2 Identify which type of contraction is shown in each of the images below. **(3 marks)**

Image A: .... Image B: .... Image C: ....

3 The image below shows someone doing a ski sit.

Which **one** of the following types of muscle contraction is happening in the lower leg muscles during a ski sit? Put a cross in the box next to the correct answer. **(1 mark)**

A ☐ Isometric

B ☐ Concentric

C ☐ Eccentric

D ☐ Fast contraction

Slow twitch muscle fibres (type I)

> **Guided**

1 Decide whether the following statements about slow twitch muscle fibres are **true** or **false**.

(4 marks)

Statement		True or false?
A	Slow twitch muscles fibres, as stated in their name, contract slowly but they can produce high amounts of force	False
B	Sprinters such as Usain Bolt (the 100 m world record holder) only use a very low amount of slow twitch muscle fibres	
C	Mo Farah (and other long-distance runners) require high amounts of type I muscle fibres	
D	Slow twitch muscle fibres can cope with prolonged activity and are slow to fatigue	

2 Give **one** example of an event that requires a high number of slow twitch muscle fibres.

(1 mark)

....

3 Give **one** example of an event that does not rely on a high number of slow twitch muscle fibres.

(1 mark)

....

4 Which of the following **two** sporting events rely on the use of slow twitch muscle fibres? Put a cross in the box next to the correct answer.

(2 marks)

A ☐ High jump

B ☐ Rugby

C ☐ Shot put

D ☐ Marathon running

E ☐ Javelin

> Remember to read the question carefully and check how many marks are available to give you an idea of the number of answers.

5 Explain why Tour de France cyclists rely on slow twitch muscle fibres.

(2 marks)

....

Fast twitch muscle fibres (type IIa)

> **Guided**

1 Which **one** of the following athletes relies mainly on fast twitch (type IIa) muscle fibres? Put a cross in the box next to the correct answer. **(1 mark)**

  A   B   C

A ☐ Jenny Meadows – 800 m runner

~~**B** ☐ Greg Rutherford – long jumper~~

C ☐ Yohan Blake – 100 m sprinter

> Think about the activity. A long jumper's event is over very quickly. Type IIa muscle fibres are used when you need energy for longer, so you know that **option B** cannot be right.

2 State the aerobic capacity of a type IIa muscle fibre. **(1 mark)**

....

3 Decide whether the following statements about fast twitch (type IIa) muscle fibres are **true** or **false**. **(3 marks)**

Statement	True or false?
A Type IIa muscle fibres are quick to fatigue	
B They produce medium amounts of force	
C They have a low speed of contraction	

4 State **two** characteristics of type IIa muscle fibres and, with reference to an example, explain how these characteristics make the muscle fibres suitable for a particular sporting activity. **(4 marks)**

....

....

....

....

....

Fast twitch muscle fibres (type IIb)

1

> Which **one** of the following athletes requires mainly fast twitch (type IIb) muscle fibres?
> Put a cross in the box next to the correct answer. **(1 mark)**

A

B

C

A ☐ Kelly Sotherton – shot-putter

B ☐ Alistair Brownlee – triathlete

C ☐ Andy Baddeley – 1500 m runner

Guided **2**

> Name **another** event in which fast twitch (type IIb) muscles are used. **(1 mark)**

High jump or .... where the athletes require very fast and .... muscle ....

3

> Decide whether the following statements about fast twitch (type IIb) muscle fibres
> are **true** or **false**. **(3 marks)**

Statement	True or false?
A Out of the three types of muscle fibres, these are the slowest to contract	
B These muscle fibres can produce high amounts of force	
C They have a strong aerobic capacity	

4

> What causes fatigue in fast twitch (type IIb) muscle fibres? **(1 mark)**

....

5

> Which **one** of the following describes the rate of fatigue in fast twitch (type IIb)
> muscle fibres? Put a cross in the box next to the correct answer. **(1 mark)**

A ☐ Quickly **B** ☐ Moderately **C** ☐ Slowly **D** ☐ They don't fatigue

55

Recruitment of muscle fibres with varied levels of muscular effort

1   Which muscle fibres are recruited first in any sporting movement?   **(1 mark)**

....

2   What muscle fibres are being recruited at the point indicated on the graph below?   **(1 mark)**

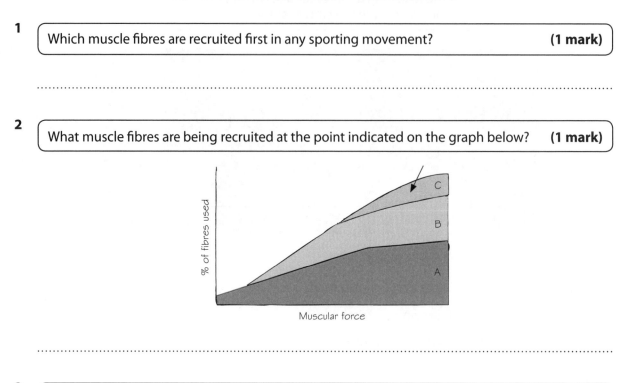

....

3   Describe what is happening at the arrow on the graph below and why.   **(2 marks)**

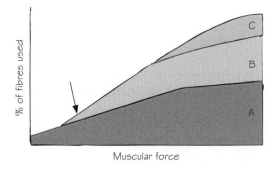

....

....

4   Circle the correct words in the following sentence.   **(1 mark)**

There is a **large/small** percentage of muscle fibres being used at point C and the type of muscle fibres being used at point C are **type I/type IIa/type IIb**.

5   The recruitment pattern of muscle fibres occurs in what type of pattern?   **(1 mark)**

....

Bones of the skeleton

1 Label the image of the skeleton with the following bones. **(8 marks)**

| Cranium | Fibula | Ulna | Sternum |
| Femur | Scapula | Patella | Vertebral column |

In the online test, you may have to drag and drop words onto a diagram.

2 Fill in the blanks in the following sentences using the correct bones listed in **Question 1**. **(2 marks)**

The .... is found in the top of the leg. The tibia and .... are found in the lower leg.

3 What is another name for the cranium? **(1 mark)**

....

Different types of bone

1 Which **one** of the following images shows a long bone? Put a cross in the box next to the correct answer. **(1 mark)**

Figure 1   Figure 2   Figure 3

A ☐ Figure 1

B ☐ Figure 2

C ☐ Figure 3

> **Guided**

2 Complete the table with an example of each type of bone. **(4 marks)**

Bone type	Example
Short	Carpals; tarsals
Sesamoid	
Irregular	
Flat	

3 Decide whether the following statements are **true** or **false**. **(3 marks)**

Statement	True or false?
A Short bones are usually cube shaped	
B The sternum is an example of a long bone	
C The function of a flat bone is to aid movement	

The axial and appendicular skeleton

Below is a diagram of a skeleton. Use this to answer the questions on this page.

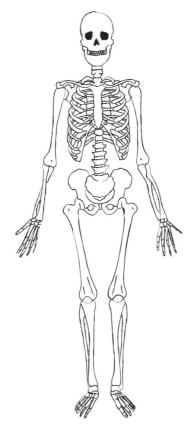

1

(a) Colour in the image above to identify the bones in the axial skeleton. **(1 mark)**

(b) Using a different colour, identify the bones in the appendicular skeleton. **(1 mark)**

> Ensure you note on the diagram the different colours you've used for the axial and the appendicular skeleton.

Guided **2**

List the bones in the axial skeleton. **(4 marks)**

1   Cranium   3 ....

2 ....   4 ....

3

List **four** of the bones found in the appendicular skeleton. **(4 marks)**

1 ....

2 ....

3 ....

4 ....

Structure of the rib cage and vertebral column

1
> How many pairs of ribs are there in total?   **(1 mark)**

....

Guided   **2**   Label the following on the diagram of the rib cage.

> **(a) Seven** pairs of true ribs.
>
> **(b) Three** pairs of false ribs.
>
> **(c) Two** pairs of floating ribs.   **(3 marks)**

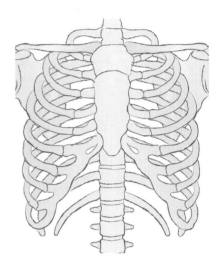

3   Label the following on the diagram on the vertebral column.

> **(a)** Label the **five** regions in the vertebral column.   **(5 marks)**

> **(b)** Label the number of vertebrae found in each region.   **(5 marks)**

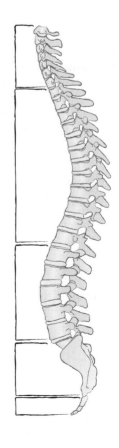

Functions of the skeletal system 1

Guided **1**

> Use the correct words from the box below to complete the blanks in the following sentence about the functions of the skeleton. **(5 marks)**

The skeleton provides *protection* for the .... For example, the cranium provides

protection for the .... and the rib cage provides protection for the .... and

....

brain	skull	vital organs	neck
kidneys	heart	protection	lungs

2

> Decide whether the following statements are **true** or **false**. **(3 marks)**

Statement	True or false?
A The skeleton provides muscle attachment sites to prevent movement at a joint	
B The vertebral column protects the spinal cord	
C Ligaments pull on bones to create movement	

3

> Explain how muscles create movement at a joint. **(2 marks)**

....

....

4

> Complete the table below to show how the functions of the skeleton can be applied to a range of different sports activities. **(6 marks)**

Function	Range of sports activities
Protection	Heading a ball in football, tackling in rugby
	Any movement created happens because of this function, including running, jumping, changing direction
Shape	
	Handstand in gymnastics, sprinting, jumping
	The continuous production of these cells means that oxygen can continue to be transported around the body during sporting activities when it is needed more
Storage of minerals	

Functions of the skeletal system 2

1   State which function of the skeleton is being demonstrated in the image below.   **(1 mark)**

....

2   Give **one** example of when your skeleton may change shape.   **(1 mark)**

....

3   What is produced inside the bone marrow of a long bone?   **(1 mark)**

....

Guided   **4**   Name the **four** minerals that are stored in bones.   **(4 marks)**

1   Phosphorus

2   ....

3   ....

4   ....

5   The spinal cord is protected by which of the following? Put a cross in the box next to the correct answer.   **(1 mark)**

A ☐ Cranium   B ☐ Obliques

C ☐ Vertebral column   D ☐ Pelvis

Classifications of joints

1 What are fixed joints also known as? Put a cross in the box next to the correct answer.

(1 mark)

A ☐ Cartilaginous joints

B ☐ Synovial joints

C ☐ Immoveable joints

D ☐ Static joints

2 Give **one** example of a fixed joint. **(1 mark)**

....

3 What are freely moveable joints also known as? Put a cross in the box next to the correct answer. **(1 mark)**

A ☐ Cartilaginous joints

B ☐ Synovial joints

C ☐ Immoveable joints

D ☐ Slightly moveable joints

> When trying to answer multiple-choice questions, start with the answers you **know** are wrong and go from there.

4 How many types of freely moveable joints are there? **(1 mark)**

....

Guided

5 Decide whether the following statements are **true** or **false**. **(3 marks)**

Statement		True or false?
A	The joints between the vertebrae allow slight movement because they are condyloid joints	
B	Freely moveable joints have the smallest range of movement of all the classifications of joints	
C	Slightly moveable joints are used most during sporting activities to create movement at joints	False

Types of freely moveable joints

> **Guided**

1 **(a)** Which type of freely moveable joint is found at the shoulder joint shown in **Figure 1**? **(1 mark)**

Figure 1

Ball and ....

(b) Give **one** example of where you would find this type of freely moveable joint. **(1 mark)**

....

2 Which type of freely moveable joint is found at the joint, shown in **Figure 2**, that allows the performer to bend her arm at the elbow? **(1 mark)**

....

....

Figure 2

3 Which **one** of the following types of joint is the intercarpal joint in the hands? **(1 mark)**

A ☐ Hinge joint   B ☐ Ball and socket joint

C ☐ Saddle joint   D ☐ Gliding joint

4 Which **one** of the following is an example of a condyloid joint? **(1 mark)**

A ☐ Neck joint   B ☐ Shoulder joint

C ☐ Wrist joint   D ☐ Knee joint

5 Which **one** of the following is an example of a saddle joint? **(1 mark)**

A ☐ Wrist joint   B ☐ Carpometacarpal joint of the thumb

C ☐ Elbow joint   D ☐ Knee joint

Types of cartilage

Guided 1 How many types of cartilage are there in the human body? **(1 mark)**

Three types

2 Which type of cartilage is described by the following characteristics? **(1 mark)**

It is found in tendons and in intervertebral discs. It contains collagen fibres and is tough.

....

3 Give **one** example of how the type of cartilage described above can protect a performer in a particular sport. **(1 mark)**

....

4 What is another name for hyaline cartilage? **(1 mark)**

....

5 Where would you find hyaline cartilage? **(1 mark)**

....

6 Identify **two** reasons why it is important to have hyaline cartilage in this location? **(2 marks)**

....

....

7 Which type of cartilage can be found in the external part of the ear and the epiglottis? **(1 mark)**

....

8 Which **one** of the following is particularly important in protecting the ankle, knee and hip joints of the sprinters in the image? **(1 mark)**

A ☐ Hyaline cartilage   B ☐ Elastic cartilage

C ☐ Fibrocartilage   D ☐ Collagen fibres

Synovial joint structure

1   Using the labels in the box below, complete the labels on the diagram of a synovial knee joint.
    (4 marks)

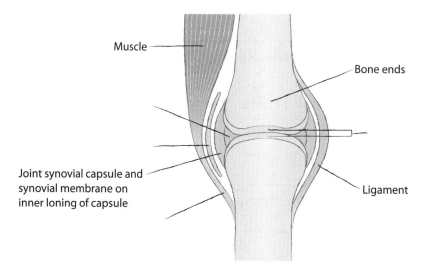

Muscle

Bone ends

Joint synovial capsule and synovial membrane on inner loning of capsule

Ligament

Bursa	Synovial fluid
Hyaline cartilage	Tendon

Guided   2   Match the synovial joint structure to its correct description and function.   **(6 marks)**

Joint structure	Description/function
Joint synovial capsule	Fills the joint capsule and lubricates the joint helping to reduce friction
Synovial membrane	Connective tissue made up of elastic fibres that join bone to bone and hold together the bones that form the joint
Bursa	Soft tissue that lines the joint synovial capsule and protects the joints from wear and tear
Synovial fluid	Tough, white, fibrous cords of connective tissue made from collagen that help to attach muscle to bone
Tendons	Fluid-filled sac between the tendon and bone that helps reduce friction at the joint
Ligaments	Fibrous tissue that encases a synovial joint

Joint movements 1

1   What is the term that describes a **decrease** in the angle of a joint?   **(1 mark)**

....

2   Give **one** example of a joint at which this movement occurs.   **(1 mark)**

....

3   **Figure 1** shows flexion at the shoulder and hip joint.

   Is this statement **true** or **false**?   **(1 mark)**

....

Figure 1

4   What is the term used to describe an **increase** in the angle of a joint?   **(1 mark)**

....

5   **Figure 2** shows a high jumper taking off.

   Which joint movement is happening at the right hip and which joint movement is happening at the left hip?   **(2 marks)**

....

....

....

Figure 2

6   Using an appropriate example, explain how flexion and extension are used in practice.   **(2 marks)**

Flexion and extension are used in many sporting movements and involve the shoulder, elbow,

hip and knee. A specific example is when ....

....

....

67

Joint movements 2

Guided **1** Describe the term abduction in relation to joint movement and give **one** example of a sporting activity in which it occurs. **(2 marks)**

Abduction is .... This movement can occur when you are reaching up to block an opposing player's shot in netball.

2 Describe the term adduction in relation to joint movement and give **one** example of a sporting activity in which it occurs. **(2 marks)**

....

3 Describe where abduction is occurring in the image opposite. **(1 mark)**

....

....

....

4 Using the words in the box below, complete the blanks in the sentence about rotation. **(4 marks)**

Rotation is when the .... at a .... moves around its own ....

making a .... movement.

joint   circular   bone   axis

5 Give **one** example of when rotation occurs in a particular sporting activity. **(1 mark)**

....

6 Circumduction is made up of a combination of movements.

Which **one** of the following combinations of movements is it made up of? **(1 mark)**

A ☐ Flexion, rotation, extension and abduction

B ☐ Adduction, abduction, elevation and depression

C ☐ Flexion, abduction, extension and adduction

D ☐ Flexion, plantarflexion, dorsiflexion and extension

Joint movements 3

1 Which joint movement is being demonstrated at the ankle in **Figure 1**?   **(1 mark)**

....

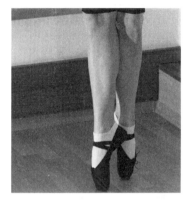

Figure 1

> Try to learn the joint movements as pairs. That will help you with questions like these.

2 Which joint movement is being demonstrated at the ankle in **Figure 2**?   **(1 mark)**

....

Figure 2

3 In which joint does elevation and depression occur?   **(1 mark)**

....

Guided **4** Give **one** example of a sporting movement in which elevation and depression are used.
   (1 mark)

Elevation and depression occur in any sporting movement that raises the shoulders, such as

....

Had a go ☐ Nearly there ☐ Nailed it! ☐

Joint movement and muscle group contractions related to sports performance

Guided

1 **Which one of the following muscles creates flexion at the elbow joint? (1 mark)**

A ☐ Triceps
B ☐ Deltoids
C ☐ Pectorals
D ☒ Biceps

Think about the muscles you find in your arms.

2 Which muscle is contracting concentrically to create the movement at the right knee shown in **Figure 1**? **(1 mark)**

A ☐ Rectus abdominis
B ☐ Quadriceps
C ☐ Hamstrings
D ☐ Erector spinae

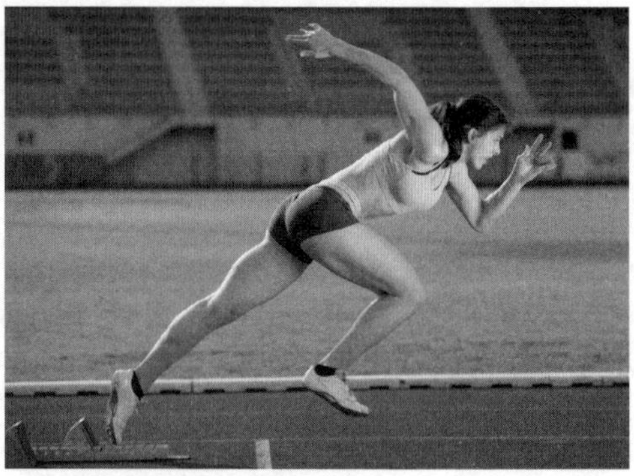

Figure 1

3 Which **two** muscles are contracting concentrically to create the movement at the right ankle shown in **Figure 2**? **(2 marks)**

A ☐ Gastrocnemius and quadriceps
B ☐ Gastrocnemius and hamstrings
C ☐ Gastrocnemius and soleus
D ☐ Soleus and hamstrings

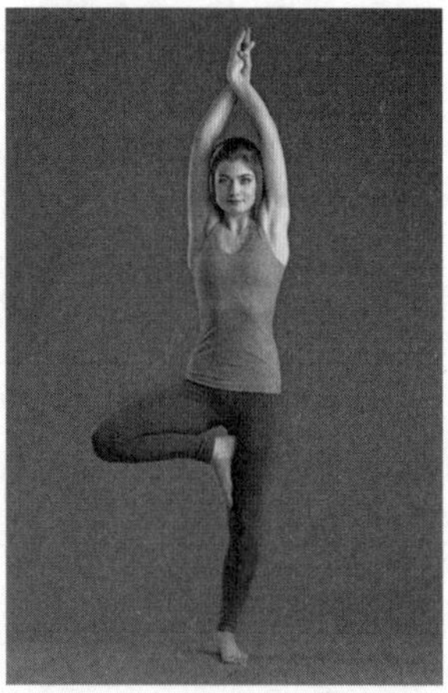

Figure 2

4 Which muscle contracts concentrically to allow for elevation at the shoulder joint? **(1 mark)**

A ☐ Latissimus dorsi
B ☐ Trapezius
C ☐ Deltoids
D ☐ Obliques

5 Which muscle contracts concentrically to allow for extension at the hip joint? **(1 mark)**

A ☐ Quadriceps
B ☐ Hamstrings
C ☐ Abdominals
D ☐ Gluteus maximus

Structure of the heart

Guided 1   Label the diagram of the heart below with the following structures.   **(6 marks)**

Tricuspid valve	Semi-lunar valve	Septum
Left ventricle	Right atrium	Coronary artery

2   Label the diagram with the main blood vessels leading to and from the heart.   **(4 marks)**

Aorta	Pulmonary veins
Pulmonary artery	Vena cava

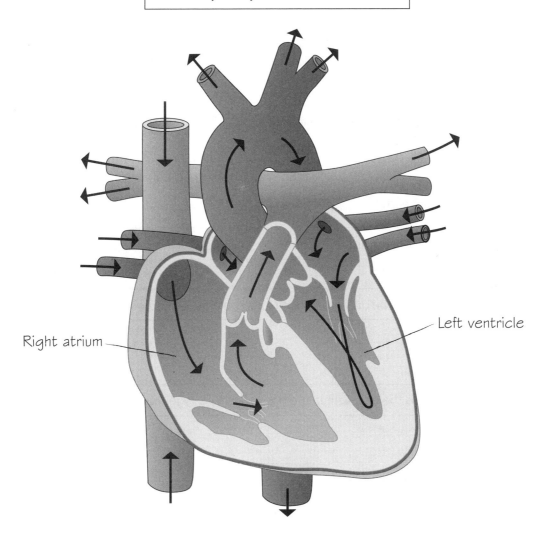

Right atrium

Left ventricle

Types of blood vessels

1 How many types of blood vessel are there in the human body? **(1 mark)**

☐ **A** Three   ☐ **B** Four   ☐ **C** Five   ☐ **D** Two

2 Decide whether the following statements are **true** or **false**. **(4 marks)**

Statement	True or false?
A Arteries are smaller versions of arterioles	
B Blood is carried away from the heart under high pressure	
C Capillaries are smaller versions of veins	
D Blood in veins is under high pressure	

Guided **3** Using the words in the box below, complete the following sentences about the differences between arteries and veins. **(6 marks)**

Arteries have thick muscular and elastic walls. They carry blood under .... pressure

.... the heart.

Veins have .... walls than arteries. They carry blood under .... pressure

towards **the heart.**

towards	thinner	low	thick	high	away from

4 Which artery is the only artery **not** to carry oxygenated blood? **(1 mark)**

....

5 Which vein is the only vein in the body to carry oxygenated blood? **(1 mark)**

....

6 Give **two** reasons why veins have valves. **(2 marks)**

....

....

7 Describe **two** roles of a capillary. **(2 marks)**

....

....

Functions of the cardiovascular system

1 One of the main functions of the cardiovascular system is transport.

> Why does the cardiovascular system need to transport oxygen? **(1 mark)**

....

2 | What is the main waste product that the cardiovascular system needs to remove? **(1 mark)**

....

Guided   **3**

> Using the words in the box below, fill in the blanks in the sentence about the cardiovascular system's transport function. **(4 marks)**

nutrients	hormones
organs	cells

The cardiovascular system transports .... to .... and cells. It also provides

.... with ....

4 | If a sports performer sustains an injury that causes them to bleed, how does the cardiovascular system respond to stop the bleeding? **(1 mark)**

....

5 | Which blood cells play a role in protecting the body against disease and infection? **(1 mark)**

....

Functions of the cardiovascular system – thermoregulation

1   What is the constant internal temperature that the body tries to maintain? **(1 mark)**

....

Guided 2   Which **one** of the following statements defines vasodilation? Put a cross in the box next to the correct answer. **(1 mark)**

A ☐ Blood vessels increase in diameter to reduce blood flow

B ☐ ~~Blood vessels decrease in diameter to reduce blood flow~~

C ☐ Blood vessels increase in diameter to increase blood flow

D ☐ Blood vessels decrease in diameter to increase blood flow

> Remember that vasodilation is related to reducing heat loss. Reducing blood flow would not help with this so you know **option B** is not the answer.

3   State **two** of the ways the body will respond when the internal temperature of the body rises above its normal level. **(2 marks)**

....

....

4   Define 'vasoconstriction'. **(1 mark)**

....

5   When would vasoconstriction of the blood vessels need to take place and what would happen? **(3 marks)**

....

....

....

....

6   What happens to the muscles when they are trying to generate heat? **(1 mark)**

....

Structure of the respiratory system

1 Using the **four** labels below, label the diagram of the respiratory system.   **(4 marks)**

| Epiglottis | Bronchioles |
| Alveoli | Intercostal muscles |

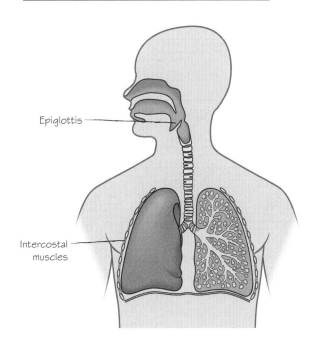

Epiglottis

Intercostal muscles

2 Outline **three** functions of the nasal cavity.   **(3 marks)**

....

....

3 **(a)** Where would you find pleural membranes and pleural fluid?   **(2 marks)**

....

(b) Identify **two** purposes of pleural fluid.   **(2 marks)**

....

4 Identify **one** purpose of the rings of hyaline cartilage in the trachea.   **(1 mark)**

....

Functions of the respiratory system 1

1   What is the process of breathing in known as? Put a cross in the box next to the correct answer.   **(1 mark)**

A ☐ Expiration

B ☐ Transpiration

C ☐ Perspiration

D ☐ Inspiration

> Guided

2   Choose the correct words from the box below to complete the blanks in the sentences about breathing in.   **(6 marks)**

increases	decreases	into	out of	external
internal	downwards	expands	upwards	increase

During the process of breathing in, the external intercostal muscles contract and raise the rib cage ....

> Think about the motions your own body goes through when breathing in and out.

The diaphragm contracts .... and .... the size of the thoracic cavity. The

lung volume increases and the pressure .... This causes air to rush into the lungs.

3   What is the process of breathing out known as? Put a cross in the box next to the correct answer.   **(1 mark)**

A ☐ Expiration

B ☐ Transpiration

C ☐ Perspiration

D ☐ Inspiration

4   Circle the correct words in the following sentence.   **(2 marks)**

When the lung volume decreases, the pressure **increases/decreases**.
This causes air to be forced **in/out** of the lungs.

Functions of the respiratory system 2

1 What does the term 'gaseous exchange' mean in relation to the respiratory system? **(2 marks)**

....

....

2 What is the name of the process in which gases pass between the bloodstream and the cells or alveoli? **(1 mark)**

....

Guided **3** Using the words in the box below, fill in the blanks in the sentences about the process of gaseous exchange. Use the diagram to help you. **(6 marks)**

deoxygenated	alveoli	carbon dioxide
inspiration	diffusion	expiration

During gaseous exchange, oxygen rich air enters the lungs by inspiration. Oxygen then passes

by .... through the capillary walls into the blood. It then circulates in the

bloodstream to where it is required by the body's cells. When it returns to the lungs the blood is

.... and contains more carbon dioxide, which is a waste product created

during the process of respiration. The carbon dioxide diffuses into the alveoli and is breathed out

by ....

Oxygen-rich blood is carried to the pulmonary vein and back to the heart to be circulated around the body

Carbon dioxide-rich blood from the pulmonary artery

Carbon dioxide rich air leaves the lungs through expiration

Alveolus

Capillary wall

Blood cells in the bloodstream

Carbon dioxide passes (diffuses) through the capillary walls and enters the alveolus

Oxygen passes (diffuses) through the capillary walls into the bloodstream

Functions of the cardiorespiratory system

1 Which **two** systems work together to make the cardiorespiratory system? **(2 marks)**

....

....

> **Guided**

2 Using the words in the box below, complete the blanks in the following sentences about the cardiorespiratory system. **(6 marks)**

lungs	blood	oxygen
energy	carbon dioxide	body

One of the main functions of the cardiorespiratory system is to pump *blood* to the heart,

.... and the .... to ensure that gaseous exchange

can take place.

The cardiorespiratory system also needs to supply *oxygen* to the body tissues so that

.... can be produced.

Another function of the cardiorespiratory system is to remove ...., which

is a waste product of respiration.

3 Blood is oxygenated when it returns to the heart from the body.

Is this statement **true** or **false**? **(1 mark)**

....

4 Carbon dioxide is unloaded from the muscles into the blood stream as a waste product to be returned to the heart and then sent to the lungs to be expired.

Is this statement **true** or **false**? **(1 mark)**

....

Exam skills 1

For each question, choose and answer and put a cross in the box next to the correct answer.

1 Which **two** of the following are characteristics of slow twitch muscle fibres (type I)?

  A ☐ They contract slowly

  B ☐ They have medium aerobic capacity

  C ☐ They produce explosive power

  D ☐ They have high aerobic capacity

  E ☐ They produce medium amounts of force

2 Which **two** of the following statements is **true**?

  A ☐ True ribs are comprised of 4 pairs

  B ☐ Floating ribs are comprised of 12 pairs

  C ☐ True ribs are attached to the vertebrae and the sternum

  D ☐ Floating ribs are comprised of 2 pairs

  E ☐ False ribs are only attached to the vertebrae at the back

3 What joint movement occurs at the ankle joint when a basketball player is taking off for a jump shot?

  A ☐ Rotation

  B ☐ Extension

  C ☐ Adduction

  D ☐ Plantarflexion

4 Which **two** of the following statements best describes the joint synovial capsule?

  A ☐ It is covered with slippery cartilage

  B ☐ It encases the joint

  C ☐ It is made of collagen, so it is tough and strong

  D ☐ It provides strength to prevent injuries

  E ☐ It is comprised of the synovial membrane

5 Which **one** of the following is **not** a mineral stored in bones?

  A ☐ Calcium

  B ☐ Sodium

  C ☐ Potassium

  D ☐ Bone marrow

Exam skills 2

1 Define the term 'concentric muscle contraction'. **(1 mark)**

....

2 What is the role of the septum in the heart? **(1 mark)**

....

3 Explain why the pectoral muscles are important when doing press-ups. **(2 marks)**

....

....

4 Explain why white blood cells are important for keeping us healthy. **(2 marks)**

....

....

> Remember when you're asked to 'explain' in your answer you should use words like 'because' and 'therefore'.

Exam skills 3

1 Explain how the cardiorespiratory system allows the body to take part in endurance exercise.

(8 marks)

....

....

....

....

....

....

....

....

....

2 Explain how thermoregulation maintains a constant temperature in the body.   **(8 marks)**

....

....

....

....

....

....

....

....

....

3 Explain the structure of a synovial joint and how this links to joint movement.   **(8 marks)**

....

....

....

....

....

....

....

Unit 1: Practice assessment test

You have 1 hour to complete this assessment.

The total number of marks is 50.

Answer ALL questions.

1

Which **one** of the following best describes agility? Put a cross in the box next to the correct answer. **(1 mark)**

A ☐ The ability to make a controlled change of direction at speed

B ☐ The ability to move multiple body parts together and under control

C ☐ The time taken to perform an action

D ☐ The ability to maintain the centre of gravity over a base of control

2   The image shows someone taking part in a flexibility test.

What is the test in the image called?   **(1 mark)**

....

3

Which **one** of the following is a type of balance? Put a cross in the box next to the correct answer. **(1 mark)**

A ☐ Still

B ☐ Dynamic

C ☐ Steady

D ☐ Proprioceptive

4

Complete the following definition by selecting **two** of the terms from the box below.   **(2 marks)**

.... are where the pace is gradually increased from a standing or rolling

start to jogging, then to striding, and then to a ....

Stretching	Walking	Acceleration sprints	Extended sprints
Maximum sprint	Running	Hollow sprints	Sprint intervals

5   What does 'PNF' stand for?   **(1 mark)**

....

6   Ali is training for a decathlon.

> Which scale could Ali's trainers use to measure his exercise intensity? Put a cross in the box next to the correct answer.   **(1 mark)**

A ☐ Willis scale

B ☐ Kington scale

C ☐ The Borg (RPE) scale

D ☐ Mann scale

7
> Describe the method for the Illinois agility run test.   **(2 marks)**

....

....

8
> Explain why collecting baseline fitness testing data may be important.   **(2 marks)**

....

....

9   Eleanor is 20 years old and wants to work in her aerobic training zone.

> What are the upper and lower ends of her aerobic heart rate zone?
> Show your workings in the box below.   **(2 marks)**

Upper end ....

Lower end ....

10 The performers in Figure 1 and Figure 2 require high levels of fitness to be able to participate in their chosen sports.

Figure 1

Figure 2

> Identify **one** component of skill-related fitness that **both** performers will use to achieve success in their event. **(1 mark)**

....

11 > Explain how **one** component of physical fitness is used in **each** of the events shown in **Figures 1** and **2**. **(4 marks)**

....

....

....

....

12 > State **one** area of physical fitness that is important for a netball player and explain your choice. **(3 marks)**

....

....

....

13 Coaches measure the fitness of their performers using a range of fitness tests.

In the table below:

(a) Identify the correct test for the aspect of fitness being measured.   **(3 marks)**

(b) Name a sport where performers would find the test useful.   **(3 marks)**

Aspect of fitness	Name of test	Activity where performers would find the test useful
Speed		
Quadriceps power		
Aerobic endurance		

14 Explain how plyometric training helps to prepare a performer for a sport-specific performance of your choice.   **(2 marks)**

....

....

15 Using a sporting example, explain what is meant by the terms 'reliability' and 'validity'.   **(4 marks)**

....

....

....

....

16 Using a sporting example, describe how it is possible to have validity without reliability.   **(2 marks)**

....

....

....

....

17 Explain how interval training would be different for performers wishing to develop speed compared to those wishing to develop aerobic endurance.   **(4 marks)**

....

....

....

....

18 Bicep curls and lateral raises are examples of exercises that may be found in what type of training? **(1 mark)**

....

19 Elise is taking part in a fitness training programme to improve the muscular endurance of her abdominals and her speed.

(a) Name a test that would be an appropriate measure of muscular endurance. **(1 mark)**

....

(b) Name a test that would be an appropriate measure of speed. **(1 mark)**

....

20 James is a weightlifter who wants to measure his body composition while training at his local gym. There are three main tests to measure body composition: body mass index, bioelectrical impedance analysis and skinfold testing.

Discuss the advantages and disadvantages of **each** of these tests for James. **(8 marks)**

....
....
....
....
....
....
....
....
....
....
....
....
....
....
....

Unit 7: Practice assessment test

You have 1 hour to complete this assessment.

The total number of marks is 50.

Answer ALL questions.

1 There are three classifications of joint found in the human skeleton. These are fixed, cartilaginous and synovial joints.

> Which **one** of the following is an example of a fixed joint? **(1 mark)**

A ☐ Elbow joint   B ☐ Shoulder joint

C ☐ Joints of the vertebrae   D ☐ Joints of the skull

2 The vertebral column has five regions.

> On the diagram to the right, label the regions listed in the box below. **(2 marks)**

> Thoracic   Coccyx

3 There are three different types of muscle in the human body: skeletal, smooth and cardiac.

> Provide **one** example of where **each** type of muscle can be found. **(3 marks)**

1 ....

2 ....

3 ....

4
> Using the words in the box below, correctly identify the muscles on the diagram of the muscular system. **(3 marks)**

> Obliques   Pectorals   Quadriceps

5   The image opposite shows a football player extending his leg at the knee when kicking a football.
Two muscle groups work together to allow this to happen. This is known as an antagonistic pair.

(a) Name the **agonist** as the leg straightens.
(1 mark)

....

(b) Name the **antagonist** as the leg straightens.   **(1 mark)**

....

(c) Give **one** more example of an antagonistic muscle pairing.   **(1 mark)**

....

6   There are several different parts to a synovial joint.

Which part of a synovial joint joins muscle to bone?   **(1 mark)**

....

7   The image shows an endurance cyclist. Endurance cyclists use lots of slow twitch (type I) muscle fibres.

Explain **one** characteristic of a type I muscle fibre that makes them beneficial for an endurance cyclist.   **(2 marks)**

....
....
....
....

8   There are five main types of bone in the human skeleton. Long bones are one of the types of bone in the human skeleton.

Give **one** characteristic of a long bone.   **(1 mark)**

....

9   Articular cartilage covers the articulating surfaces of bones.

> Give **two** functions of articular cartilage and explain why these functions are important in sport.   **(4 marks)**

....

....

....

....

10   A condyloid joint is one type of synovial joint.

> The wrist is an example of a condyloid joint. Give **one** other example of a synovial joint.
>   **(1 mark)**

....

11
> Which **one** of the following is the correct description of an isometric contraction?
> Put a cross in the box next to the correct answer.   **(1 mark)**

A ☐   When a muscle shortens in length and develops tension

B ☐   When a muscle contracts but doesn't change in length

C ☐   When a muscle develops tension while increasing in length

D ☐   When a muscle contracts and then changes length

12   The image on the right shows a gym exerciser performing a lateral raise.

> Which movement pattern is happening at the shoulder joint to allow this exercise to happen?   **(1 mark)**

A ☐   Flexion   **B** ☐   Circumduction

C ☐   Adduction   **D** ☐   Abduction

13 The image below shows the various phases of a triple jump.

> Analyse how the muscles and joints interact to allow the athlete to complete the triple jump.
> **(8 marks)**

....

....

....

....

....

14 There are a number of different types of blood vessel in the circulatory system.

> **(a)** Give **one** structural characteristic of veins. **(1 mark)**

....

> **(b)** Give **one** function of veins. **(1 mark)**

....

15 > Explain the role of vasoconstriction in thermoregulation. **(2 marks)**

....

....

16 The diagram below shows the heart.

> Using the words in the box below, label the various structures of the heart. **(4 marks)**

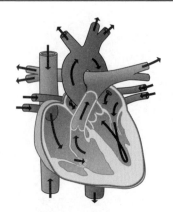

| Vena cava | Left ventricle | Pulmonary vein | Pulmonary artery |

17 The diagram on the right shows the respiratory system.

Label the diagram using the words in
box below.   **(4 marks)**

| Alveoli | Diaphragm | Bronchioles | Trachea |

18 State **two** functions of the cardiorespiratory system.   **(2 marks)**

....

....

19 Name the **two** main processes associated with the mechanics of breathing.   **(2 marks)**

....

....

20 The image below shows a process taking place within the cardiorespiratory system.

(a) What is this process called?   **(1 mark)**

....

(b) Explain how this process works.   **(2 marks)**

....

....

....

....

Alveolus

Capillary
wall

Blood cells
in the
bloodstream

Answers

The following pages contain example answers for questions in the Workbook. In many cases, they represent only one possible correct answer.

UNIT 1 ANSWERS

LEARNING AIM A

1. Aerobic endurance

1 **C** Cardiovascular fitness

2 (a) **B** Marathon runner

   (b) Marathon runners need good aerobic endurance as they perform at a moderate intensity for a long period of time. They therefore need a continual supply of oxygen and the continual removal of waste products in order to maintain a good pace in the race.

3 Aerobic endurance is the ability of the **cardiovascular** system to work efficiently, supplying **oxygen** and **nutrients** to working muscles during sustained physical activity. It is also responsible for the removal of waste products such as **carbon dioxide** and water.

2. Muscular endurance

1 **A** The ability to use voluntary muscles repeatedly over time without them getting tired

2

Performer	How muscular endurance is used in their sport
Rower	Excellent muscular endurance in the upper body and arms allows the rower to row repeatedly against the resistance of the water without tiring.
Marathon runner	Required for continual repeated stride patterns in the legs. Leg muscles need to be able to work repeatedly without fatigue to complete the distance in the quickest time.
Long-distance swimmer	Required for the continual movement of arms and legs against the resistance of the water without the onset of fatigue.

3 **A** Muscular endurance

  B Muscular strength

  C Muscular strength

  D Muscular endurance

3. Flexibility

1 Flexibility is the range of motion possible at a **joint**.

2 High jumpers require excellent flexibility in the shoulders, lower back and hips to ensure that they are able to bend their torso and legs around the bar and avoid knocking it off. Hurdlers require excellent flexibility in their hips in order to achieve the best position when travelling over the hurdles to maintain speed.

3 A 100 m sprinter needs high levels of flexibility, particularly in the hip, as flexibility increases stride length so they can cover the distance more quickly.

4. Speed

1 **A** m/s

2 Speed can be defined as **distance** travelled **divided** by the time taken. There are three basic types of speed. They are **accelerative** speed, pure speed and speed endurance.

3 Accelerative speed = Sprints up to 30 metres
  Pure speed   = Sprints up to 60 metres
  Speed endurance = Sprints with short recovery periods in-between

4

Performer	Type of speed	When it is used
100 m sprinter	Pure speed	Maximum speed is required for the duration of the race.
Long jumper	Accelerative speed	During the run-up so that they are travelling at maximum speed on take-off.
Hockey player	Speed endurance	During a game when running for the ball or chasing a tackle. There are periods of rest in-between.

5. Muscular strength

1 Muscular strength is an example of **physical** fitness.

2 Power is the ability to use muscular strength at **speed**.

3 In shot put, muscular strength is needed to maximise the distance travelled. This is important as the person who puts the shot the furthest will win.

6. Agility

1 Agility is the ability to make a controlled **change** of direction at **speed**.

2 A netball player needs to dodge quickly in order to get away from the person marking her and to get into a space to receive a pass.

3 (a) Event B (hurdler)

   (b) The competitors in event B need agility for clearing the hurdles. The competitors in event A do not have as much need for agility because they are running in a straight line with nothing in their way.

7. Balance

1 **A** Static

2 Static balance is the ability to maintain the centre of gravity over a stationary base of support. An example of this would be a headstand.
Dynamic balance is about a performer's ability to maintain their centre of gravity over a constantly moving base of support. An example of this would be a gymnast performing a cartwheel.

3 Gymnasts require excellent static and dynamic balance in order to hold positions such as handstands, cartwheels and tumbles. In the high jump, balance is needed during flight to maintain an accurate body position and increase the chance of clearing the bar.

4 One from: goal keeper; goal defence – they both need to balance on one foot in order to take a shot.

8. Coordination

1 **B** The ability to use two or more body parts together

2 Tennis = hand–eye coordination
  Football = foot–eye coordination
  Basketball = hand–to–hand coordination

3 Suitable answers include:
- The batter needs hand–eye coordination to ensure that they strike the ball accurately.
- The fielders need hand–eye coordination to ensure that they can catch any high balls directly off the bat so players can be caught out.

9. Power

1 Power = **strength** × **speed**

2 The tennis player needs power in order to make fast shots that are harder to return. Increased power means the opposition has less time to respond.
The rugby player needs power in order to make ground when tackles are attempted and so that they can get away from their opponent and keep possession of the ball.

3 A javelin thrower needs power in order to throw the javelin as far as possible. A strong upper body and fast movement in the throwing arm will ensure maximum power is transferred to the object when it is thrown.

10. Reaction time

1 Reaction time is the time taken for a sports performer to respond to a **stimulus** and the initiation of this **response**.

2 (a) A Sprinter
  (b) The sprinter would require better reaction times as they need to respond directly to a stimulus (the starting gun) at the start of their event. If they do not react quickly their performance will suffer. The shot-putter does not need to respond to any immediate stimuli – they just have to throw within a particular time.

11. The importance of fitness components for success in sport

1 **B** Muscular endurance in the upper arms

2 It allows them to dodge quickly away from players and evade tackles.

3

Sports example	Aspect of fitness that is important	Why it is important
Gymnast	Flexiblity	It allows them to move their joints through a large range of movement and hold more extreme body positions.
Discus thrower	Balance	It helps them to stay in the circle at the end of the throw.
Football goalkeeper	Reaction time	It helps them respond quickly to shots on goal.

4 A football striker needs good speed and agility in order to make fast runs on the ball and to avoid being tackled by opposing players. Goalkeepers do not need to do this. Rather they need good reaction times and good flexibility. This allows them to respond quickly to shots on goal and to stretch their body to deflect shots at awkward angles.

12. Exercise intensity: heart rate

1 The number of times your heart beats in 1 minute

2 220 – age. Therefore 220 – 23 = 197, so John's maximum heart rate would be 197 bpm.

3 Beats per minute

4 It enables you to calculate heart rate training zones. These are zones within which different adaptations occur. So if you were trying to improve your aerobic endurance, your heart beat needs to be within the aerobic training zone. Without knowing your maximum heart rate, you wouldn't be able to work this out.

13. Exercise intensity: the Borg (RPE) scale

1 Rating of perceived exertion

2 A circle around ratings 12–14 is acceptable

3 1 The Borg (RPE) scale can be used to estimate heart rate and as a tool for calculating training zones.
  2 It can be used in various training environments and does not require any equipment.

14. Exercise intensity: training zones

1 **D** 60–85% of HRmax

2 The sprinter requires anaerobic fitness in order to perform at their maximum and so needs to be training without the presence of oxygen in the anaerobic training zone. They do not require high levels of aerobic endurance and therefore working in the aerobic training zone would not be relevant.

3 220 – 36 = 184
60% of 184 = 110
85% of 184 = 156
Therefore the heart rate zone would be 110–156 bpm.

15. Basic principles of training

1 Frequency, Intensity, **Time**, Type

2 **A** Frequency
  B Time
  C Intensity
  D Type

3 Naseem could adjust her training by:
  (a) using training aids to add resistance and increase intensity.
  (b) adding in some quicker or longer swims.
  (c) increasing the number of times she trains each week.

16. Additional principles of training 1

1 **C** Specificity

2 Fartlek training would be appropriate for a football player because the training is varied in pace. This mimics the conditions of a game. No footballer runs continuously for 90 minutes so periods of rest followed by periods of work are most similar to the requirements of the game.

3 (a) Abby should train in the pool because it is more specific to her sport. It replicates the demands and environment of her event, unlike the track which would be more appropriate for a long-distance runner.
  (b) Weights can help Abby develop muscular endurance which is an aspect of fitness that meets the specific training needs of a swimmer and so her performance will benefit.

17. Additional principles of training 2

1 To avoid injury

2 1 Increase the frequency of training – for example, training more times per week.
  2 Increase the length of time of each training session – for example, increasing sessions from 30 minutes to 40 minutes.
Other examples could include: increasing the intensity or changing the type of training.

3 The results suggest she was overloading initially to increase from level 6.3 to 7.1 but then she did not apply progressive overload as she has plateaued. This suggests she was working in a comfortable training zone.

18. Additional principles of training 3

1 **C** Designing a programme to meet the training needs and goals of the individual

2 Danuta and Edward have different training needs and goals. Danuta would need to work on developing aspects of fitness like speed and reaction times, while Edward would be better off training his aerobic endurance. If they both followed the same programme you would not expect to see improvements in one or both of their performances over time.

3 **(a)** Danuta should follow a speed-based programme.

   (b) Edward should participate in continuous training.

19. Additional principles of training 4

1 If you do not train regularly any improvements in fitness can be lost.

2 Any one from: it allows adaptation to occur; it reduces the risk of injury.

3 Kim – as her performance improved and then dropped after peaking, which is evidence of reversibility.

4 Suitable answers include: an injury, holiday, lost motivation or stopping training.

20. Additional principles of training 5

1 **A** Court work; strength work in the gym; weights for muscular endurance

2 Variation is important so that the performer does not get bored of their routine.

3 Rivka could run on the road, cross-country or in the gym on a treadmill in order to add variation.

4 Lucy could change the type of equipment that she used, such as changing from free to fixed weights. She could change or vary her training environments, such as exercising alone in a gym or exercising outdoors with friends. She could also vary the order that she completes her training session as well as changing the type of exercise that she completes. The nature of her training could also be varied, such as changing from continuous to interval training.

LEARNING AIM B

21. Circuit training

1 **A** Station 1: sit-ups

   B Station 8: tuck jumps

   C Station 5: skipping

2 You could spend more time on each station and reduce the length of the recovery period. You could repeat the circuit twice rather than just going around once. Weights could be used to increase resistance on some activities.

3 Stations 3 and 4 both exercise the same body part. This is a problem because of the risk of fatigue and injury. There needs to be some recovery time between each station. The circuit could be improved by moving station 3 to the end of the circuit after the tuck jumps.

22. Continuous training

1 Aerobic endurance

2 Suitable answers include: marathon running; long-distance swimming; endurance cyclists; triathletes.

3

Name	Age (years)	HRmax (bpm)	Aerobic zone lower limit (bpm)	Aerobic zone upper limit (bpm)
Di	68	152	91	129
Dave	50	170	102	145
Minsuh	34	186	112	158
Adam	20	200	120	170

4 You would not improve your aerobic endurance as you would be working at too high an intensity.

23. Fartlek training

1 Suitable answers include: weighted jacket, weighted training vest, harness or something similar.

2 As tennis involves players sprinting short distances in order to reach the ball, training should involve short bursts of sprinting with longer periods of jogging in-between. The length of these short bursts could be varied depending on the player's ability.

3 There are lots of changes in terrain that could be used to alter the intensity. For example, there is a hill to the left-hand side that could help to increase intensity when compared to the flat path to the right. There are also changes in terrain such as grass and a gravel path.

24. Interval training

1 Interval training involves periods of high intensity exercise followed by periods of rest or lower intensity work.

2 **(a)** Diagram B

   (b) Diagram B best represents the interval training most suitable for a sprinter. To improve speed, the best intervals need to be high intensity with short rest periods.

3 To reduce the risk of injury and to allow for recovery.

25. Plyometric training

1 **C** Hurdle jumps

2 Muscle lengthening immediately followed by muscle shortening.

3 Plyometric training would be used to increase the power generated at take-off so she could jump higher.

4 It has a high risk of injury and it is not suitable for young athletes.

26. Speed training methods

1 **C** Box sprints

2 Hollow sprints

3 Speed interval training may be used by long-distance runners because it allows them to practise exercising at a higher intensity for a longer period of time before fatigue or pain slows them down.

4 **C** Acceleration sprints

27. Flexibility training

1 Active stretching is performed without equipment and relies on internal forces to stretch the muscle. Passive stretching uses another person or object to provide resistance.

2 Benefits include reducing the risk of injury and improving performance.

3 **Proprioceptive neuromuscular** facilitation

4 Passive = C, PNF = B, Ballistic = D, Active = A

28. Weight training

1 Muscular strength and muscular endurance

2 Repetitions are the number of times a weightlifting exercise is repeated, for example, 12 reps. Sets are the number of times these blocks of exercises are completed, for example, 3 sets of 12 reps.

3 Maximum strength

4 Suitable answers include: shot-putter; discus thrower; javelin thrower.

5 When you are training for strength endurance you use a low weight but do more reps. If you are training for maximum strength, the load-to-weight ratio moves the other way and you lift heavy weights but fewer times.

LEARNING AIM C

29. Fitness testing: importance to sports performers and coaches

1 Any one from: it allows you to see if training has worked, to identify weaknesses and to design suitable future training programmes.

2 Coach: Allows the coach to monitor the effectiveness of training. If training is working then you would expect fitness test scores to improve over time.
Performer: It can be motivating because the performer can see how much they are improving as a result of their training over time.

3 (a) Training to improve upper body muscular endurance and speed have been successful.

   (b) Training to improve hamstring flexibility has not been successful.

30. Fitness testing: issues, validity and reliability

1 Validity = How accurate a test is so that it measures what it should measure
Reliability = The ability to repeatedly carry out a test and get the same result each time.

2 Anyone taking part in the test.

3 Suitable answers include: weather conditions; length and type of warm-up; diet; hydration; amount of sleep; location of testing.

4 Calibration is important because it helps to ensure accuracy. For example, a set of scales used for weighing an athlete need to be calibrated each time. If after a couple of uses they no longer return to zero, then any following weight measurements would no longer be accurate.

31. Fitness tests: skinfold testing (body composition 1)

1 C Tricep, suprailiac and thigh

2 Skinfold callipers

3

Name	Age (years)	Skinfold total (mm)	Body fat (%)
Chloe (female)	18	55	22
Ayesha (female)	26	25	12
Charlie (male)	15	120	28

4 The most concerning body fat reading would be Charlie's as his result of 31 per cent body fat would categorise him as being obese. The girls' results place them both in the ideal category.

32. Fitness tests: BMI (body composition 2)

1 Body mass index

2 C kg/m^2

3 BMI is not always an accurate measurement for measuring body composition because muscle is heavier than fat. Muscular individuals, such as boxers and weightlifters, are therefore naturally heavier even with a low percentage of body fat so BMI is not appropriate in these cases.

4 (a) $66\,kg \div (1.5 \times 1.5) = 29.3$

   (b) This would be classed as overweight.

33. Fitness tests: bioelectrical impedance analysis (body composition 3)

1 Image **B**

2 1 The equipment is very specialised and therefore expensive.
   2 It relies on the subject being well hydrated and not having done any vigorous exercise 12 hours prior to the test.

3 Being dehydrated can increase the body fat reading so it becomes inaccurate.

4 **D** Bone

34. Fitness tests: muscular endurance – abdominal

1 The sit-up test.

2 **B** reps/minute

3 Step 1: Lie on the mat with your knees bent and your feet flat on the floor.
Step 2: Fold your arms across your body. Use an assistant to time you for 1 minute.
Step 3: Complete as many full sit-ups as you can in this time. A full sit-up is one where you raise yourself up to 90° and then lower yourself back to the floor.

4 Suitable answers include: gymnastics; martial arts; diving; dance.

35. Fitness tests: muscular endurance – upper body

1 1-minute press-up test

2 Step 1: Take up a full press-up position on the mat. Your arms should be fully extended.
Step 2: Use an assistant to time you for 1 minute.
Step 3: Complete as many full press-ups as you can in this time. A full press-up is one where the elbows are bent to 90° and then fully extended.

3 In the standard test, the subject takes all of their weight on their hands and feet. In the modified version the subject is allowed to place their knees on the floor for additional support.

4 This test measures muscular endurance in the pectorals and triceps not the legs.

36. Fitness tests: speed – 35 m sprint test

1 Suitable answers include: a hurdler; a centre court netball player; a rugby winger; a sprinter; a long jumper.

2 **A** Not using a tape measure to mark out 35 m in one test
   C Doing the tests at different times of the day

3 The final score is the best of the three scores.

4 The 35 m sprint test requires participants to run in a straight line whereas the Illinois agility run test requires changes of direction.

37. Fitness tests: MSFT (aerobic endurance 1)

1 VO_2 max is the maximum amount of oxygen a person's body is able to take in and use, and is measured in ml/kg/min.

2 Multistage fitness test

3 An athlete should finish this test when they are either no longer physically able to keep up with the beeps, when they can no longer keep going or when they miss the line by the time of the beep three times.

4 The benefit of using the MSFT with a large group such as a lacrosse team is that lots of people can complete the test at the same time with very little equipment required. It is also more appropriate to the nature of the activity.

5 Any two from: the time of day the test is conducted; the terrain; the weather; whether the test is conducted indoor or outdoors; the accuracy of the measurement; the length and type of warm-up.

38. Fitness tests: forestry step test (aerobic endurance 2)

1 To help the participants step in time

2 Some people might not have the fitness or coordination to keep going for 5 minutes.

3 Step 1: Record body weight with clothing on.
Step 2: Stand directly opposite the bench and start stepping in time with the beat of the metronome.
Step 3: As soon as you start stepping, start the stopwatch. Step up and down continuously in time with the beat for 5 minutes.
Step 4: After 5 minutes, stop immediately and locate your radial (wrist) pulse.
Step 5: Fifteen seconds after stopping, count your pulse for 15 seconds and record this number.

39. Fitness tests: agility

1 **D** Illinois agility run test

2 Any two from: netball players; football players; rugby players; hockey players, etc. Or any two team sports where players need to change direction at speed.

3 Advantage: It requires minimal amounts of equipment. Disadvantge: You need someone to help you log results.

4 It replicates the movements and agility needed for a game of tennis closely.

40. Fitness tests: vertical jump test (anaerobic power)

1 Anaerobic power in the quadriceps.

2 **D** kgm/s

3 Suitable answers include:
- A basketball player. They should score highly because they use dynamic power in their quadriceps to jump high for interceptions and to shoot at goal.
- High jumpers would score well as they need to be able to run up powerfully in order to get maximum height over the bar.

4 Plyometrics training

41. Fitness tests: grip dynamometer (strength)

1 **C** It needs specialised equipment

2 It would not be accurate because the three readings were not taken with the same hand and so not with the same pressure.

3 Although the test measures strength it is specific to the arms and so would give no indication of leg strength or the effectiveness of his training programme.

4 **C** Judo player

42. Fitness tests: flexibility

1 **B** Sit and reach test

2 Gymnastics and diving

3 1 Variations in trunk and arm length can make comparisons difficult.
  2 It is not relevant to all parts of the body.

4 PNF training would help to improve flexibility. To improve scores on the sit and reach test it would need to be focused on the lower back and legs.

43. Exam skills 1

1 **C** Total

2 **B** 100 m sprinters often use continuous training

3 **B** HRmax = 220 − age

4 **A** The Jackson–Pollock nomogram

5 **D** Bounce

6 **B** Measuring what you actually say you are measuring

44. Exam skills 2

1 Test: Illinois agility run test. Method: Performers start by lying on the floor and then run around a course of cones, which forces them to make quick changes of direction. The faster the time, the better their agility.

2 122 – 173 bpm. Workings: 220 − 17 = 203. 85% of 203 = 173. 60% of 203 = 122. Therefore her training zone is between 122 – 173 bpm.

3 Progressive overload means working your body progressively harder over time so that adaptations and improvements to fitness are made. This can be done by increasing the amount of time that a person is training for so that it gets progressively harder.

4 Definition: Coordination is the ability to use two or more body parts together to ensure that tasks are performed efficiently and accurately. Why it is important: It is important for a tennis player as they need to be able to use hand–eye coordination consistently in order to strike the ball accurately in order for it to go where intended and to use hand–eye coordination to complete complex movements like the service.

45. Exam skills 3

1 **A** Illinois agility run test
  B Sit and reach test
  C Multistage fitness test

2 The Illinois agility run test may be a better measure of sprint speed for a rugby player as it involves changes of direction that are more common in a game of rugby – so it is more specific to the needs of the sport. It is very unlikely that a rugby player would sprint in a straight line for any period of time.

3 Lin has made continual improvements over time and is likely to be participating in continuous training. It is clear that this is effective and she must be applying progressive overload. Richard has not made progress over time so it is likely that he is either training for another aspect of fitness or is using an unsuitable training method. Pedro made some progress and has then experienced reversibility. It is likely that he experienced an injury midway through his training.

UNIT 7 ANSWERS

LEARNING AIM A

46. Major voluntary muscles 1

1 (a) **A** = Biceps, **B** = Triceps, **C** = Quadriceps, **D** = Hamstrings
  (b) **A** = Flexion of the arm at the elbow joint
   B = Extension of the arm at the elbow joint
   C = Extension of the leg at the knee
   D = Flexion of the leg at the knee

47. Major voluntary muscles 2

1 Trapezius

2 Any action that requires the shoulders to be pulled backwards to bring the shoulder blades closer together. For example, in swimming during the butterfly action the arms are thrown backwards; the take-back during a tennis serve; when using a seated row resistance machine or an upright row free-weights exercise.

3 Pectorals: adducts the arm at the shoulder.

4 Any action that brings the arm across the midline of the body or down to the side of the body. For example, the follow-through from a forehand drive in tennis; when using a 'pec deck' resistance machine; when doing a bench press; the forwards motion of a throw-in.

48. Major voluntary muscles 3

1 Gluteus maximus

2 **B** Extend the hip

3 Gastrocnemius

4 Any movement that requires pointing the toes. For example, pointing the toes in ballet; taking off in high jump; calf raises in the gym.

5 Deltoid

6 **C** Abducts the shoulder

49. Types of muscle

1

Type of muscle	Location	Characteristics
Voluntary	• Skeletal muscles	• Conscious control • Skeletal movement
Involuntary	• Stomach • Intestines	• Slow, rhythmic contraction • Unconscious control

2 (a) Voluntary muscle is also known as **skeletal** or **striated** muscle.
  (b) Involuntary muscle is also known as **visceral** or **smooth** muscle.

3 (a) Heart muscle is also known as **cardiac muscle**.
  (b) Heart muscle is under **unconscious** control because it needs to keep **beating** to keep us alive.

4 **C** Cardiac muscle can only be found in the heart

5 **D** Contractions are rapid and sustained

50. Voluntary muscle movements

1 **Skeletal** muscles work **together** to provide **movement** of the **joints**.

2 While one muscle contracts another relaxes to create movement. For example, during a bicep curl the bicep is the muscle contracting and the tricep is the muscle relaxing.

3 Muscles are connected to bones via **tendons**. When a muscle contracts, it **pulls** on the **tendon**, which then **pulls** on the bone to create movement.

4 **A**: Quadriceps = antagonist; **B**: Hamstrings = agonist

5 During the backward swing of a kick, the hamstring flexes the knee joint and the quadriceps relax. During the forward swing, the quadriceps contract and become the agonist and the hamstrings relax and become the antagonist.

51. Antagonistic muscle pairs

1 Biceps = Triceps
Rectus abdominus = Erector spinae
Pectoralis major = Trapezius
Quadriceps = Hamstrings

2 (a) **C** Gastrocneimus
  (b) **A** Tibialis anterior

3 Rectus abdominus and erector spinae

4 The netball player is actively using several muscle pairs during the shot. To create elbow extension, the triceps need to contract and the biceps need to relax. Any of the following are acceptable:
  • Her deltoids need to contract to flex the shoulder joint so the latissimus dorsi needs to relax.
  • The erector spinae needs to contract to help her lean backwards so the abdominals need to relax.
  • Her hamstrings need to contract and the quadriceps need to lengthen to allow for knee flexion.

52. Types of contraction

1

Type of muscle contraction	Description	Example
Concentric	When a muscle shortens and develops tension as it contracts	Biceps: when lifting a weight during a bicep curl
Eccentric	When a muscle lengthens it develops tension	Biceps: when lowering a weight during a bicep curl
Isometric	When a muscle contracts but does not shorten and there is no movement	Biceps: when lifting the weight so the elbow is at 90 degrees but then holding it in that position. The holding position is when the muscle is contracting isometrically

2 A = Isometric; B = Eccentric; C = Concentric

3 **A** Isometric

53. Slow twitch muscle fibres (type I)

1 **A** False **B** True **C** True **D** True

2 Any prolonged activity, for example: a marathon, a triathlon, long-distance swimming.

3 Events over short- to medium-length distances, for example: any sprint event (100 m, 200 m, 400 m or 800 m) or any power event (e.g. power lifting, high jump, shot put).

4 **B** Rugby **D** Marathon running

5 These fibres have a high aerobic capacity, are highly resistant to fatigue and have a slow force of contraction. As a result, they allow Tour de France cyclists to complete endurance events effectively.

54. Fast twitch muscle fibres (type IIa)

1 **A** Jenny Meadows – 800 m runner

2 Medium aerobic capacity

3 **A** False **B** True **C** False

4 Type IIa muscle fibres have fast contractions and are fairly resistant to fatigue. An 800 m runner requires fast contractions because 800 m is a quick event but they also need to be able to sustain these contractions for longer than a 100 m runner.

55. Fast twitch muscle fibres (type IIb)

1 A Kelly Sotherton – shot-putter

2 High jump or long jump where athletes require very fast and powerful muscle contractions.

3 A False
   B True
   C False

4 Lactic acid

5 A Quickly

56. Recruitment of muscle fibres with varied levels of muscular effort

1 Type I

2 Type IIb

3 Type IIa muscle fibres are starting to be recruited because the intensity of activity is increasing.

4 There is a **large** percentage of muscle fibres being used at point C and the type of muscles being used a point C are **type IIb**.

5 Ramp-like recruitment pattern

57. Bones of the skeleton

1

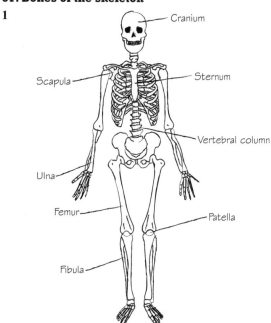

2 The **femur** is found in the top of the leg. The tibia and **fibula** are found in the lower leg.

3 Skull

58. Different types of bone

1 A Figure 1

2

Bone type	Example
Short	Carpals; tarsals
Sesamoid	Patella
Irregular	Vertebrae or some facial bones
Flat	Cranium; ribs; scapula; sternum; pelvic girdle

3 A True
   B False
   C False

59. The axial and appendicular skeleton

1 (a) and **(b)**

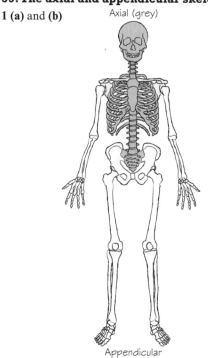

2 Cranium, rib cage, sternum and vertebral column.

3 Any four from: scapula, clavicle, humerus, radius, ulna, pelvis, tibia, fibula, patella, femur.

60. Structure of the rib cage and vertebral column

1 12

2

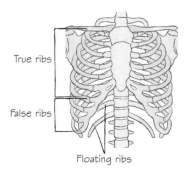

3 (a) and **(b)**

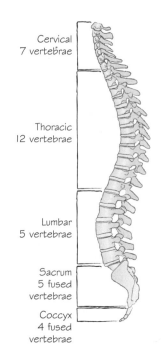

61. Functions of the skeletal system 1

1 The skeleton provides **protection** for the **vital organs**. For example, the cranium provides protection for the **brain** and the rib cage provides protection for the **heart** and **lungs**.

2 **A** False   **B** True   **C** False

3 Muscles are joined to bones via tendons. When a muscle pulls on a tendon it in turn pulls on the bone to create movement.

4

Function	Range of sports activities
Protection	Heading a ball in football, tackling in rugby
Muscle attachment and movement	Any movement created happens because of this function, including running, jumping, changing direction
Shape	In basketball and netball it helps if you are tall for shooting the ball. In horse racing, the smaller you are the better because the horse doesn't have to carry as much weight
Support	Handstand in gymnastics, sprinting, jumping
Blood production	The continuous production of these cells means that oxygen can continue to be transported around the body during sporting activities when it is needed more
Storage of minerals	All sports require the nervous system to create muscle contraction. All the minerals that the skeletons stores are used in these processes

62. Functions of the skeletal system 2

1 Support

2 During growth

3 Red blood cells

4 Phosphorus, calcium, potassium and sodium

5 **C** Vertebral column

63. Classifications of joints

1 **C** Immoveable joints

2 Cranium or sacrum

3 **B** Synovial joints

4 Six types

5 **A** False   **B** False   **C** False

64. Types of freely moveable joints

1 (a) Ball and socket
  (b) Hip joint

2 Hinge joint

3 **D** Gliding joint

4 **C** Wrist joint

5 **B** Carpometacarpal joint of the thumb

65. Types of cartilage

1 Three types

2 Fibrocartilage

3 Helps to absorb shock from any movement that has an impact – for example, sprinting, jumping and throwing.

4 Articular cartilage

5 Found on the articulating surface of bones

6 Any two from: aids shock absorption; protects bones from wear and tear; ensures supple movements; provides support to joints.

7 Elastic cartilage

8 **A** Hyaline cartilage

66. Synovial joint structure

1

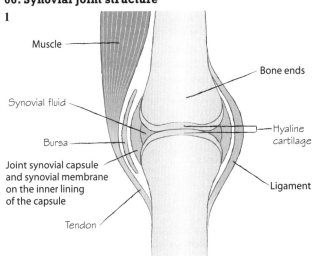

2

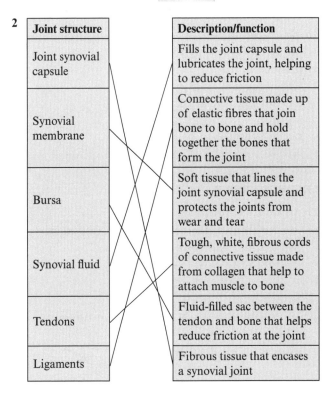

Joint structure	Description/function
Joint synovial capsule	Fills the joint capsule and lubricates the joint, helping to reduce friction
Synovial membrane	Connective tissue made up of elastic fibres that join bone to bone and hold together the bones that form the joint
Bursa	Soft tissue that lines the joint synovial capsule and protects the joints from wear and tear
Synovial fluid	Tough, white, fibrous cords of connective tissue made from collagen that help to attach muscle to bone
Tendons	Fluid-filled sac between the tendon and bone that helps reduce friction at the joint
Ligaments	Fibrous tissue that encases a synovial joint

67. Joint movements 1

1 Flexion

2 Any one from: shoulder, elbow, hip or knee

3 False. It shows abduction.

4 Extension

5 Right hip = flexion; left hip = extension.

6 Flexion and extension are used in many sporting movements and involve the shoulder, elbow, hip and knee. A specific example is when a player passes a basketball to a teammate. The player flexes at the elbows to bring the ball into the body and then quickly extends at the elbow to push the ball away from them to another player.

68. Joint movements 2

1 Abduction is movement away from the midline of the body. This movement can occur when you are reaching up to block an opposing players' shot in netball.

2 Adduction is movement towards the midline of the body – for example, when a swimmer pulls the water back in breaststroke.

3 Abduction is occurring in the left arm of the player in the dark shirt.

4 Rotation is when the **bone** at a **joint** moves around its own **axis** making a **circular** movement.

5 Rotation occurs during many movements involving the shoulder or the hip. Examples could include serving in tennis, swimming using front crawl, changing direction in team sports, and throwing across your body in rugby, basketball or netball.

6 **C** Flexion, abduction, extension and adduction

69. Joint movements 3

1 Plantarflexion

2 Dorsiflexion

3 Shoulder

4 Elevation and depression occur in any sporting movement that raises the shoulders, such as shoulder shrugs, throw-ins for football, high jump and shot put.

70. Joint movement and muscle group contractions related to sports performance

1 **D** Biceps

2 **C** Hamstrings

3 **C** Gastrocnemius and soleus

4 **B** Trapezius

5 **D** Gluteus maximus

LEARNING AIM B

71. Structure of the heart

1 One mark awarded for each correct label. (Either semi-lunar valve is acceptable.)

2 One mark awarded for each correct label.

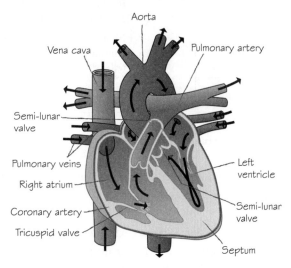

72. Types of blood vessels

1 **C** Five

2 **A** False   **B** True   **C** False   **D** False

3 Arteries have **thick** muscular and elastic walls. They carry blood under **high** pressure **away from** the heart. Veins have **thinner** walls than arteries. They carry blood under **low** pressure **towards** the heart.

4 Pulmonary artery

5 Pulmonary vein

6 To prevent backflow of blood and help venous return

7 Any two from: to allow diffusion of oxygen; to allow removal of carbon dioxide; to allow diffusion of waste products; to allow removal of waste products.

73. Functions of the cardiovascular system

1 Oxygen is needed by the cells for energy production.

2 Carbon dioxide

3 The cardiovascular system transports **hormones** to **organs** and cells. It also provides **cells** with **nutrients**.

4 Platelets gather at the site of the injury forming a clot to stop the blood flowing out of the blood vessel.

5 White blood cells

74. Functions of the cardiovascular system – thermoregulation

1 37°C

2 **C** Blood vessels increase in diameter to increase blood flow

3 Sweating and vasodilation

4 Arterioles under the surface of the skin decrease in diameter.

5 When body temperature has fallen. To decrease blood flow to the capillaries under the surface of the skin, reducing the amount of heat that is lost through the skin.

6 The muscles shiver to generate heat.

75. Structure of the respiratory system

1 One mark awarded for each correct label.

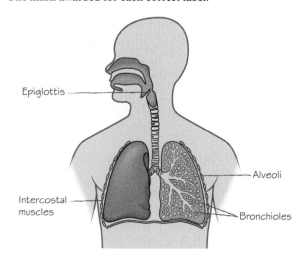

2 The air is warmed by the blood in the nasal cavity; the air is filtered by the cilia; the air is moistened by mucus.

3 (a) Pleural membranes are found in the linings of the lungs and the thoracic cavity. Pleural fluid is found between the membranes.

(b) Pleural fluid provides lubrication and allows the lungs to inflate and deflate without causing damage.

4 The rings of hyaline cartilage in the trachea prevent the trachea from collapsing.

76. Functions of the respiratory system 1

1 **D** Inspiration

2 During the process of breathing in, the **external** intercostal muscles contract and raise the rib cage **upwards**. The diaphragm contracts **downwards** and **increases** the size of the thoracic cavity. The lung volume increases and the pressure **decreases.** This causes air to rush **into** the lungs.

3 **A** Expiration

4 When the lung volume decreases, the pressure **increases.** This causes air to be forced **out** of the lungs.

77. Functions of the respiratory system 2

1 The process by which oxygen passes into the body and is circulated around the body, and by which carbon dioxide is removed from the blood for expiration.

2 Diffusion

3 During gaseous exchange, oxygen rich air enters the lungs by **inspiration.** Oxygen then passes by **diffusion** through the capillary walls into the blood. It then circulates in the bloodstream to where it is required by the body's cells. When it returns to the lungs the blood is **deoxygenated** and contains more **carbon dioxide**, which is a waste product created during the process of respiration. The carbon dioxide diffuses into the **alveoli** and is breathed out by **expiration.**

78. Functions of the cardiorespiratory system

1 Cardiovascular system and respiratory system

2 One of the main functions of the cardiorespiratory system is to pump **blood** to the heart, **lungs** and the **body** to ensure that gaseous exchange can take place. The cardiorespiratory system also needs to supply **oxygen** to the body tissues so that **energy** can be produced. Another function of the cardiorespiratory system is to remove **carbon dioxide**, which is a waste product of respiration.

3 False

4 True

79. Exam skills 1

1 **A** They contract slowly   **D** They have high aerobic capacity

2 **C** True ribs are attached to the vertebrae and the sternum
   D Floating ribs are comprised of 2 pairs

3 **D** Plantarflexion

4 **B** Encases the joint
   E It is comprised of the synovial membrane

5 **D** Bone marrow

80. Exam skills 2

1 When a muscle shortens in length and develops tension.

2 The septum separates the two sides of the heart.

3 They are important because in order to complete a press-up we need to abduct our arm at the shoulder so we can push or lift our body off of the floor, so without the pectorals we would not be able to complete the press-up.

4 White blood cells are important for keeping us healthy because they produce antibodies that destroy the harmful microorganisms that invade the body and can cause infection and disease.

81. Exam skills 3

1 In order for us to take part in endurance training the cardiorespiratory system works to ensure that the body is supplied with adequate amounts of oxygen and nutrients to maintain performance. When there isn't enough oxygen in the blood, a signal is sent to the brain that makes you start to breathe in. Air containing oxygen is inhaled and enters the lungs after travelling through the respiratory structures into the lungs. Once in the lungs, air passes in to the alveoli. Capillaries are the cardiovascular system's point of contact with the respiratory system, as they run along the walls of the alveoli. To re-oxygenate blood, oxygen passes through the membrane of the alveoli, through the capillary wall and into the blood. This process is called diffusion. When in the bloodstream, oxygen is then transported around the body through the blood vessels so that oxygen can be transported to active tissues. The second part of this process is where carbon dioxide passes in the opposite direction; from the capillary, through the membrane of the alveoli and then into the lungs. As the amount of carbon dioxide in your lungs is too high at this point, your body starts to breathe out (or exhale) so that the carbon dioxide is removed. All of this process happens simultaneously and is involuntary; without this, we would not be able to continue to take part in endurance activities.

2 Thermoregulation is the process by which the body maintains a constant 37°C. It is important to do this because the body will cease normal functioning if it becomes too hot or too cold. When the body becomes too cold, it increases body temperature by vasoconstriction (narrowing of arterioles) occurring to decrease the blood flow to the surface of the skin. This increases core temperature by redirecting blood flow to the core and preventing heat loss through radiation (heat energy given off by the body). You may then start to shiver, which is an involuntary action by the body to increase heat. Subcutaneous fat insulates the body and so helps to maintain your temperature.

When the body becomes too hot, vasodilation (opening up of arterioles) happens to promote blood flow to the surface of the skin and heat loss through radiation. This helps to cool the body down. Sweat glands produce sweat which then evaporates, cooling the body.

3 Synovial joints are surrounded by a joint capsule. This is a collection of connective tissues that bind bone ends together. The joint capsule is lined by synovial membrane, which is a soft tissue that prevents wear and tear on the joint by secreting synovial fluid. Synovial fluid eases joint movement by preventing friction. Synovial joints also have ligaments and tendons that play a role in movement. Ligaments join bone to bone and provide the stability required for effective joint movement. Tendons join muscle to bone, aiding movement by pulling on the bone in order to produce movement when acted upon by a muscle. Synovial joints also have different types of cartilage (for example, fibrocartilage and articular cartilage) that acts as a shock absorber and reduces friction which can cause joint damage during sporting actions.

82. Unit 1: Practice assessment test

1 **A** The ability to make a controlled change of direction at speed

2 Sit and reach test

3 **B** Dynamic

4 Acceleration sprints, maximum sprint

5 Proprioceptive neuromuscular facilitation

6 **C** The Borg (RPE) scale

7 On 'go' participants get up and run around the course,

following the red line, as quickly as possible. The stopwatch is stopped and their time recorded when they pass the finish cone.

8 It can be used by coaches to measure the progress made by a performer during training and can show if training is targeting the correct areas of fitness.

9 220 – 20 = 200. 60% of 200 = 120. 85% of 200 = 170. Therefore, her aerobic training zone lies between 120 and 170 bpm.

10 Power

11 Speed would be used by the sprinter in order to cover distance in the quickest time as this will allow them to win their race. Speed in netball is used for getting away from defenders quickly in order to create space to receive a pass.

12 Agility is important to the netball player and not the sprinter because the netball player has to change direction and dodge away from players in order to create space. The sprinter does not have to worry about other people and does not have to change direction – therefore it would not be important.

13

Aspect of fitness	Name of test	Activity where performers would find the test useful
Speed	35 m sprint test	Hurdles or similar
Quadriceps power	Vertical jump test	High jump or similar
Aerobic endurance	Multistage fitness test	Marathon running

14 Plyometric training involves lots of bounding and jumping activities. It can be used by high jumpers to help improve the height and power of their take-off jump, which makes it easier for them to clear the bar.

15 Reliability refers to the ability to repeat a test over time and get the appropriate results so that they can be accurately compared, such as a sprinter undertaking the 35 m sprint test three times under the same conditions. Validity refers to the ability of the test to measure what it says it is measuring, so the sprinter would not take the press-up test as it is not valid for their sport.

16 You can have a set of weighing scales that clearly measure weight but which have been calibrated incorrectly and do not go back to zero each time they are used. Therefore the weight they are showing is not reliable although the scales are valid for what they are trying to test.

17 If you wanted to improve aerobic endurance then periods of work would be longer but performed at a moderate intensity. Athletes wanting to improve their speed would use shorter work intervals but would perform at close to their maximum.

18 Weight training

19 (a) Sit-up test or press-up test
(b) 35 m sprint test

20 Calculating body mass index (BMI) is a simple measure that can easily check if James is overweight, it does not require him finding any specialist equipment. The test will also shows whether James has an increased risk of cardiovascular disease. However James should be aware that the BMI measure incorporates the weight of muscle

and so can give an overweight or obese reading for muscular individuals. This could be a problem for James as he is a weightlifter and so is likely to be muscular.

Bioelectrical impedance analysis requires a specialist, expensive machine that James may not have access to. The test results rely on the subject being well hydrated and not having done any exercise or eaten beforehand. However, the main advantage of BIA is that, as it only measures body fat, it is more suitable for athletes which would suit James.

The skinfold test is a simple test to administer. It uses skinfold callipers so James would need to be able to source these and find an assistant to help him. If it is carried out properly, with readings taking at three sites, then it is a reliable measure of body fat. The disadvantage is that James may have to adjust his clothing to allow the measurements to be taken by an assistant and he may find this intrusive.

As James wants to do a test at his local gym he would be best using skinfold testing. However, BIA would also be suitable for him as a weightlifter if he could find somewhere to implement the test.

87. Unit 7: Practice assessment test

1 D Joints of the skull

2

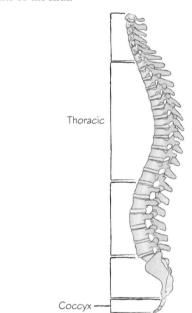

Thoracic

Coccyx

3 Skeletal = any muscle attached to bone to create movement, e.g. biceps. Smooth = intestines or stomach. Cardiac = heart.

4

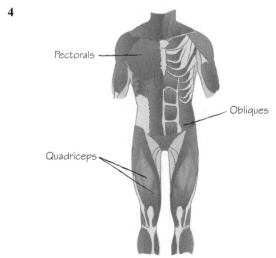

Pectorals

Obliques

Quadriceps

5 **(a)** Quadriceps

(b) Hamstrings

(c) Any pair from: biceps and triceps; pectorals and trapezius; rectus abdominis and erector spinae.

6 Tendons

7 They are slow to fatigue which allows the cyclist to continue for a long period of time as required by his event.

8 The ends of the bones are covered in articular cartilage.

9 Articular cartilage protects the joint from wear and tear. This is important because in sport the joints are required to move more frequently so the cartilage protects the joint from becoming damaged quickly. Cartilage also acts as a shock absorber. This is important because during sports performance the amount of force applied to the joints is greater, for example during jumping or running. This prevents all the force from travelling directly into the joint and damaging it.

10 Any one from: ball and socket; pivot; saddle; gliding; hinge.

11 **B** When a muscle contracts but doesn't change in length

12 **D** Abduction

13 The hips flex when the leg travels from back to front due to the contraction of the quadriceps. The hip extends as the triple jumper pushes on the ground so the other leg can come forwards; the gluteus maximus is the muscle that creates hip extension.
The knee extends when the hip is flexed at the front of the body; the quadriceps are responsible for knee extension. The knee flexes when the jumper plants his foot on the floor and when the leg is lifting off the ground at the back and travelling forwards with hip flexion. The hamstrings contract to create knee flexion.
The ankle dorsiflexes and plantarflexes during the movement. When the triple jumper plants his toes down onto the board and when he pushes off, the ankle travels from plantarflexion, into dorsiflexion and then into plantarflexion again. The gastrocnemius and soleus are responsible for plantarflexion of the ankle.
During the last phase of the movement the athlete needs to flex the vertebral column to lean as far forward as possible. The rectus abdominis creates flexion of the vertebral column.

14 **(a)** Thin walls

(b) Veins carry blood back to the heart.

15 Blood vessels called arterioles under the skin constrict. This decreases blood flow to the capillaries under the surface of the skin to prevent heat loss through radiation.

16 One mark awarded for each correct label.

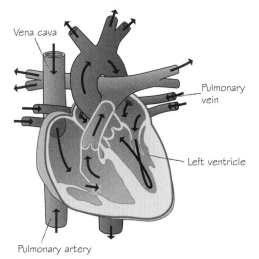

17 One mark awarded for each correct label.

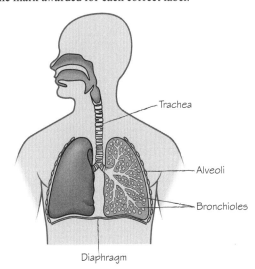

18 Any two from: blood flow through the heart; body and lungs; supplying oxygenated blood to body tissues; taking up oxygen into the body in order to produce energy; unloading carbon dioxide, a waste product of respiration, from the body.

19 Inspiration and expiration.

20 **(a)** Gaseous exchange

(b) Oxygen is breathed in through the process of inspiration and enters the lungs. Oxygen then passes by diffusion from the alveoli in the lungs to the blood and is circulated around the body. Carbon dioxide is returned to the lungs and is removed from the blood into the alveoli to be breathed out.

Your own notes

Your own notes

Your own notes

Your own notes